THE ALLYN AND BACON
SERIES IN QUANTITATIVE
METHODS FOR BUSINESS
AND ECONOMICS

ALLYN AND BACON, INC.

BOSTON

R. STANSBURY STOCKTON

CONSULTING EDITOR

PROBABILITY:
An Introduction
with Applications

ALBERT J. SIMONE

Professor of Quantitative Methods
Director, Quantitative Management Program
Boston College

TO MY PARENTS

PREFACE

Excellent books dealing with the mathematical theory of probability are readily available today. Some of these contain applications in business and economics. Since they deal with the mathematical theory, they have a mathematical prerequisite, generally, of at least one year of the calculus. Also readily available are excellent one- and two-semester texts on statistical method which treat probability and which do not have a calculus prerequisite. Why, then, have we prepared a book on probability?

Our answer is twofold. First, many businessmen and business students do not now, and never will, have the required background in the calculus. Thus, the first category of texts mentioned above is useless to them. Second, the noncalculus statistics texts contain many topics in addition to probability, e.g., descriptive statistics and time series and regression analysis. As a result, the basic structure of probability, which underlies all statistical theory and method, is often clouded and not fully appreciated as a valuable tool of analysis in innumerable management situations.

The purpose of this book, then, is to make available to the noncalculus but rigorous reader a clear introduction to the theory of probability. Since probability is the main stream flowing through every page, the reader must come away with a true appreciation of the power of the concept. But the book is more than a theoretical introduction; it is also applicable in the real world. The usefulness of the probability concept is

realistically illustrated by major text applications in the areas
of inventory control, quality control, equipment selection, machine set-up, scrap allowance, and acceptance sampling (including acceptance/rectification and AOQL), and by carefully constructed exercises dealing with these areas and also with such
concepts as the flow of funds, the acid test ratio, the evaluation
of alternative investment opportunities, stock market predic-
tions, the introduction of new products, advertising effectiveness, the development of promotional strategy, personal inter-
viewing, and the interpretation and design of samples for
market surveys.

Moreover, we have tried to write a book which represents
a proper balance between the "modern" and the "traditional"
approaches. On the modern side, the central theme is decision-making under uncertainty. We introduce the concept of a
random variable as early as possible, and use it in all subse-
quent discussions. We have tried hard to distinguish between
the random variable itself and the value of the random variable, much as modern mathematics seeks to distinguish between a function and the value of the function. The reader will
also find extended discussions of many operations research
and management science methods. For example, expected
value analysis, Monte Carlo simulation, and queuing models
are treated in some detail; moreover, prior and posterior
probabilities are defined, Bayes' theorem is derived, and the
concept of the value of perfect information is developed.

On the traditional side, we spend a good deal of time on
hypothesis testing, type 1 and 2 errors, the operating characteristic curve, and sample design for single and double
sampling plans.

Because the concept and definition of probability are the
fundamental building blocks in this book, they are slowly and
painstakingly developed in Chapter 2. However, the tempo and
the required amount of sustained attention increase progres-
sively after Chapter 2. The basic probability theorems are
not presented all at once as soon as the probability definition
is available; rather, major applications requiring only the
definition of probability and of a random variable are first
presented. Then the various probability theorems are developed as they are needed for various applications. In this way,
the practical-minded reader is introduced to major applications as soon as possible.

Many of these concepts and principles are presented in an environment which is simulated by the binomial probability model, but they are presented in general, so that the binomial model becomes merely the vehicle for exposition. The reader can then go on to more advanced and expanded texts and apply these very same concepts and principles to a wide variety of probability models. We hope that this book, by integrating theory and application, will serve as the motivation for this other, perhaps not otherwise contemplated, worthwhile task.

As a final feature, the book is entirely self-contained, i.e., nowhere do we say "It can be proved that . . ." without developing the proof ourselves. And as we mentioned before, this self-containment is provided within a noncalculus framework (we require the calculus just once, in a footnote to Chapter 6).

Because of the selection of major applications, this book can be appropriately considered as a supplementary text in a course in Production Management. Because of the choice of exercises, this book can also serve as a supplementary text in courses in Finance, Marketing, and in a general Management course which treats all the functional areas. Because of the generalized probability approach, it can be considered as a supplementary text in an introductory Statistics course, particularly one in which it is desirable to treat a wide variety of business applications. Because of the stochastic models and techniques developed, it can also be considered as a supplementary text in an Operations Research or Quantitative Methods course. Finally, we hope that thoughtful businessmen, facing the necessity of making decisions in an environment of uncertainty, will find this work generally useful.

Albert J. Simone

CONTENTS

2

PROBABILITY CONCEPTS AND DEFINITIONS

3

RANDOM VARIABLES

6

PROBABILITY MODELS FOR SCRAP ALLOWANCE AND QUEUING PROBLEMS

7

BINOMIAL PROBABILITY MODEL FOR ACCEPTANCE SAMPLING

1 ▶ UNCERTAINTY IN BUSINESS DECISION-MAKING

1.1 STOCHASTIC VERSUS DETERMINISTIC DECISION SITUATIONS

Business firms must constantly make decisions. These decisions generally are made in either one of two types of situations. One type, called a deterministic situation, represents an environment which approaches certainty. That is, before the decision is made, all relationships relevant to the decision problem are known exactly, and the values of all relevant variables are specified precisely. In this case, it is often possible to make a decision which will always turn out to be the best decision that could have been made. Linear programming is one technique which can be very fruitfully applied in this type of situation.

The other type of decision-making situation is called a stochastic situation. Here, the environment is one of

1

uncertainty. That is, the relationships relevant to the decision problem may not be known exactly. Moreover, the values
of the relevant variables are produced by stochastic processes (we shall clarify this term shortly), with the conse-
quence that, prior to the making of a decision, these values
are not precisely known. In this case, whether a given decision will turn out to be the best decision is not known until
after it has been implemented.

Probability theory is extremely helpful in analyzing
stochastic decision situations. This book is concerned with
developing this theory and showing how it can be used to solve
stochastic problems typically and frequently found in business.
In the process, this book will also develop in detail some of
these major business applications.

The remainder of this chapter will be devoted to clarify-
ing the nature of stochastic decision processes.

1.2   DECISION VALUES AND THE DECISION PROCESS

We indicated at the outset that business firms must continually make decisions. Now we shall examine this decision
process more closely.

1.21   Decision Values.

By a decision, we mean the conscious
selection of one policy or course of action from among numerous alternatives. This selection will be made prior to some
experiment, i.e., prior to the performance of some act. We
use the term "decision value" to denote a number[1] which is
associated with the desirability of the results connected with a
given decision. For example, a specific dollar profit might be
the decision value (the higher the profit the more desirable
the decision) in a given problem, while a specific dollar cost

---

[1] In a later chapter we shall consider decision values which cannot be simply stated as single numbers, which require a more
complex formulation.

might be the decision value (the lower the cost the more desirable the decision) in another problem. The actual magnitude of the decision value depends on both the decision made
prior to the experiment and the specific outcome of the experiment.

1.22 An Illustration.

Assume that a firm knows that the
daily demand for its perishable product will be either 0,1,2,
or 3 units. Each unit stocked at the beginning of a day costs $2
and sells for $5, with no salvage value for units left unsold at
the end of the day. The firm must decide how many units to
stock per day. Since stocking more than 3 units is certain to
result in a profit of $-2 for each unit over 3, we assume the
rational firm will not consider stocking more than three units.
This leaves four alternative courses of action open to the firm
(it can decide to stock either 0,1,2, or 3 units), and the firm's
decision involves a selection of one of these. Once the firm
has decided on a course of action (made a decision), an experiment will be performed and the outcome of the experiment
observed. In the present case, the relevant experiment consists of examining the sales record for this commodity at the
end of the day. Four outcomes are possible, viz., either 0,1,2,
or 3 units will have been demanded.

As indicated above, the actual magnitude of the decision
value will depend on both the particular course of action (i.e.,
the stock level) selected and the outcome of the experiment
(i.e., the number of units demanded). Since there are four
possible courses of action and, for each of these, four possible
outcomes for the experiment, there are 4 × 4 = 16 possible
decision values (some of which may be identical). Table 1.1
summarizes these possible decision values.

Each entry in this table is determined from one of the
following equations

$$\underline{P} = 5\underline{D} - 2\underline{Q} \qquad \underline{D} < \underline{Q} \qquad (1.1)$$
$$\underline{P} = 3\underline{Q} \qquad \underline{D} \geq \underline{Q} \qquad (1.2)$$

where

$\underline{P}$ denotes total profit
$\underline{D}$ denotes daily demand
$\underline{Q}$ denotes number of units stocked

TABLE 1.1

POSSIBLE DECISION VALUES
FOR INVENTORY PROBLEM

Outcome (Daily Demand) D	Course of Action (Stock Level)			
	0	1	2	3
0	0	-2	-4	-6
1	0	3	1	-1
2	0	3	6	4
3	0	3	6	9

If the number of units demanded is less than the number stocked, then Eq. (1.1) is used; if the number demanded is equal to or greater than the number stocked, Eq. (1.2) is employed. For example, if Q = 3 units are stocked but only D = 2 units are demanded, Eq. (1.1) will be used, and the total profit determined as total revenue ($5D$ = 5 × 2 = 10) minus total cost ($2Q$ = 2 × 3 = 6), i.e.,

$$P = 5D - 2Q$$
$$= 5 \times 2 - 2 \times 3 = 4$$

This is the entry recorded in the last column, third row of Table 1.1. If, on the other hand, the number of units demanded were greater than the number stocked (e.g., if D = 3 and Q = 2), the firm would make a profit of $3 on each unit it had stocked and its total profit can be determined from Eq. (1.2) as

$$P = 3Q = 3 \times 2 = 6$$

which is the entry recorded in the last row, third column of Table 1.1. The reader can verify the other entries in this table using Eqs. (1.1) and (1.2).

1.23   The "Best Decision".   For the moment, let the "best decision" be that course of action (that value of Q) which results in the greatest decision value, given the observed outcome of the experiment. In the preceding illustration, what is the best decision?

If we were told the outcome that would occur when the experiment is performed (the number of units that would be demanded), we could make the best decision (the decision that results in the greatest decision value) each day. For example, if we were told that we would observe $\underline{D}$ = 3, then we would stock $\underline{Q}$ = 3 and obtain $\underline{P}$ = 9, which is the maximum $\underline{P}$ for $\underline{D}$ = 3 (compare the entries in the bottom row of Table 1.1). However, when we make a decision we do not know the precise value of $\underline{D}$ that will be observed at the end of the day. All we know is that the number of units demanded will be some integer between 0 and 3, i.e., $0 \leq \underline{D} \leq 3.$

Hence, our decision, whatever it is, may or may not be "best", in the sense indicated above. That is, since the outcome generated by the experiment is unknown prior to the making of a decision, the decision value that will result, once a decision is made and an experiment performed, is also unknown in advance.

1.24 Rational Decisions.   In these instances, can a rational decision be made? The answer is "quite often". Moreover, probability theory typically provides the modus operandi which makes this affirmative reply possible. This theory is applicable when the experiment associated with the decision process is a "stochastic experiment". The meaning of this term will be clarified in the following section.

First we shall summarize the attributes of the decision process described in this section:

    a. Typically, a decision involves a choice of one from a number of alternative courses of action.
    b. After a decision has been made, an experiment will be performed and one out of a number of alternative outcomes will be observed.
    c. The decision value depends on both the decision made and the outcome of the experiment.
    d. For a given outcome, different decisions will typically lead to different decision values.
    e. For a given decision, different outcomes will typically lead to different decision values.
    f. Since the outcome of the experiment is unknown prior to the making of a decision, the decision value that will result is uncertain.

g. If the experiment is stochastic, probability theory
can facilitate the making of a rational decision.

1.3   STOCHASTIC EXPERIMENTS, OUTCOMES, AND EVENTS

The concept of "chance" is fundamental to any discussion
of probability and decision-making under uncertainty. Unfor-
tunately, this concept cannot be easily and concisely defined.
However, it can be readily understood by illustration. Before
proceeding with this illustration, we shall introduce some
helpful terminology.

<u>1.31   Terminology</u>.   Let the term "experiment" denote the
performance of an act; e.g., an experiment might represent
the tossing of a single unbiased die, the selection of a card
from a standard deck of shuffled playing cards, the selection
and inspection of an electric motor from a recent shipment of
100 such motors, or the examination of the record of the number of loaves of bread sold yesterday in the Ace Supermarket.
Let the term "outcome" denote the result of the experiment. For example, if the experiment is the tossing of a
single die, there are six possible outcomes, viz., a one-, two-,
three-, four-, five-, or six-spot. If the experiment is the selection of a card from a standard deck of shuffled playing
cards, there are 52 possible outcomes. If the experiment is
the selection of an electric motor from a shipment of 100 such
motors, there are 100 possible outcomes (since any one of the
100 motors might be selected). And if the experiment is the
examination of the record of the number of loaves of bread
sold yesterday, the outcome might be any integer from zero
to the maximum number of loaves stocked by the store.
Finally, let the term "event" describe a set of one or
more outcomes, such that each outcome in the set possesses
an identical distinguishing feature uniquely associated with
the event. To illustrate, in the die experiment, an event could
be described by "greater than four"; in this case two outcomes, the five- and six-spot, possess this distinguishing
feature and therefore belong to the set described by the

event. In the card experiment, the event described by "a
spade" contains 13 outcomes (2 through the ace of spades),
and the event described by "an ace of spades" contains just
one outcome. In the electric motor experiment, if 20 of the
100 motors are defective, the event described by "a defective
motor" contains 20 outcomes. In the bread sales experiment,
the event described by "more than two but less than five" is
defined by a set of two outcomes, viz., "three loaves were
sold" and "four loaves were sold".

1.32   Chance.   In the die and card experiments, what determines the number of spots which turns up and the particular
card which is drawn? Assuming no trickery on the part of
the experimenter, try as we may we can find no known reason
or assignable cause to account for the occurrence of any given
outcome or event in preference to the others. For example,
if a two-spot turns up on the throw of the die, and if we know
the die is "loaded", or if we know the die has a two-spot painted
on each of its six surfaces, we can assign a cause to account
for the observed outcome. But if the die is a standard "fair"
die and if it is tossed in an unbiased manner, we can not formulate a logical argument to account for this particular outcome in preference to any of the other possible outcomes.
In such situations, we say that chance determines the outcome
of the experiment or of the event associated with the experiment.

Thus, chance is the term used to denote the process by
which an outcome or event is generated from an experiment,
assuming no known reasons or assignable causes are available to account for the particular outcome or event observed
when the experiment is performed.[2] As this implies, in the
electric motor and bread examples introduced above, if there
are no known reasons to account for the particular outcomes
observed, these experiments are also generated by chance.

Experiments, outcomes, and events governed by chance
are called chance experiments, chance outcomes, and chance

---

[2] This is not to say that all possible outcomes in a chance experiment are equally
likely to occur. We shall fully discuss this point later.

events. In the literature today, the terms "random", "probabilistic", and "stochastic" are synonymous for the term "chance". In what follows, we shall use the particular term typically employed in the given context.

Before proceeding, the reader should be quite certain that he fully understands the specific meanings we attach to the terms experiment, outcome, event, chance (i.e., stochastic, random, probabilistic), and chance or stochastic experiment.

We turn, in the next section, to a discussion of the likelihood of the various outcomes of a stochastic experiment.

1.4   EVENTS AND THEIR LIKELIHOOD

In a deterministic situation, the decision value associated with a given decision is typically known with certainty before the relevant experiment is carried out, while in a stochastic situation the decision value is known only after the experiment has been completed and the particular outcome recorded. That is, in a stochastic situation, the decision value is never known with certainty prior to the experiment. However, experience, objective and/or subjective, would indicate that some outcomes and events, and therefore some decision values, are more likely than others.

To illustrate, assume that a firm's monthly sales over the past five years ranged between $2 million and $10 million, with a monthly average of $6 million. Assume that over this period there have been no significant trend, cyclical, or seasonal influences. In the absence of any abnormal conditions, most persons, with no more information than that just given, would say that next month sales of $6 million are more likely than sales of $100 million.

In the same fashion, most persons would tell you that the selection of a spade, in a single draw from a standard deck of shuffled playing cards, is more likely than the selection of an ace of diamonds. A gambler will tell you that throwing a seven with a pair of dice is more likely than throwing a twelve. A baseball fan will tell you that in his next time at bat Willie Mays is more likely to hit a home run than is Don Drysdale. An insurance man will tell you that a child who is two years old today is more likely to live until the age of 70 than he is to live until the age of 110. A traveler will say that rain today is more likely in Boston, Massachusetts, than in Stanford, California. And so on.

An experiment can be constructed for each of the preceding examples. Specifically, these would be, in order, examining the firm's sales record next month, drawing a single card from a deck of cards, tossing a pair of dice, examining the statistics for the next games of Mays and Drysdale, investigating the age at death of the two year old child, and examining the weather reports for Boston and Stanford. All of these experiments have three things in common: 1) they generate more than one possible outcome (event); 2) the event that will occur is uncertain; 3) intuitively, some of these outcomes (events) appear more likely than others.

The theory of probability provides a means of attaching precise numerical measures to the likelihoods of the various possible events of a stochastic experiment. This system of measures is the basis of management decision-making under uncertainty, i.e., in stochastic situations.

In the next chapter we shall develop the basic concepts of probability theory. Succeeding chapters will apply this basic theory and, where necessary, supplement it.

1.5 DISCUSSION AND REVIEW QUESTIONS

1. Distinguish between stochastic and deterministic situations.

2. What determines the magnitude of an observed decision value?

3. If a decision involves a choice of one from among seven courses of action, and if the corresponding experiment can yield eight possible outcomes, how many decision values are possible?

4. Why is the "best decision" (in the sense used in the chapter) uncertain before a stochastic experiment is performed but perfectly certain afterwards?

5. What are the basic attributes of a decision process?

6. Distinguish between the terms outcome, event, and experiment. Give several illustrations of each.

7. What do we mean when we say that "chance" generates the outcomes possible in an experiment?

2 ► PROBABILITY CONCEPTS AND DEFINITIONS

2.1 MOTIVATION

In this chapter we shall define probability and discuss some of the attributes of this definition. We shall also learn how to assign numerical measures of probability to the events associated with a wide variety of experiments.

2.2 PROBABILITY AND LIKELIHOOD

Given any experiment, the probability of a particular event occurring can be loosely defined as the likelihood of that event occurring. When we use likelihood in this sense, we require something more precise than "very likely" or "not very likely." That is, to be useful in decision-making we require a _measure_ of likelihood which will enable us to compare the likelihood of any given event with the likelihoods of all other events. Moreover, we want more than just a ranking or ordering of the likelihoods of the possible events. It is not enough to say, for example, that drawing a spade from a standard deck of playing cards is more likely than drawing an ace, and that drawing an ace is more likely than drawing a king of diamonds. We would like a measure of _how much_ more likely it is to draw a spade than an ace, _how much_ more likely it is to draw an ace than a king of diamonds, and _how much_ more likely it is to draw a spade than a king of diamonds. For example, is the event "a spade" twice as likely as "an ace", or two-and-a-half times as likely? We shall soon learn how to answer questions such as these.

However, before proceeding, the reader should be certain that he fully understands the interpretations given to the terms experiment, outcome, event, and stochastic in Chapter 1. To recapitulate briefly, an experiment refers to the performance of some act, an outcome is the result of the experiment, and an event is a set of one or more outcomes, each of which possesses a common distinguishing feature.

Moreover, in the remainder of this book, the reader should note that every experiment referred to is a stochastic experiment. We need to know more about the characteristics of such experiments. The next three sections deal with the three types of stochastic experiments relevant in discussions of the theory of probability. We shall call these three types of experiments a priori experiments, _empirical_ experiments, and _subjective_ experiments.

2.3   A PRIORI EXPERIMENTS

A priori experiments possess the following attributes:

   (a) Before the experiment is actually performed, it is
       possible to draw up a _collectively exhaustive_ list of
       outcomes, i.e., a list which includes all of the out-
       comes possible from the experiment. Any outcome
       not on the list cannot possibly occur, and any out-
       come which can possibly occur is on the list.

(b) All outcomes on the list just described are <u>mutually</u> <u>exclusive</u>, i.e., if any one of them occurs in an experiment, it is impossible for any of the others to occur simultaneously. Hence, if we know which outcome did occur, we automatically know which outcomes did not occur.

(c) The outcomes in the collectively exhaustive and mutually exclusive list of outcomes just described are <u>equally</u> <u>likely</u>. That is, there is no physical factor associated with either the experiment or the set of outcomes that would cause any one outcome to occur more frequently than any other in the long run.

The following two examples illustrate these attributes.

2.31 <u>Card Example</u>. Assume an experiment consists of drawing a single card from a shuffled deck of playing cards. A collectively exhaustive list of 52 outcomes is specified by noting the denomination and suit of each card (e.g., three of diamonds, king of spades). These outcomes are mutually exclusive; if, say, the four of clubs is selected, none of the other 51 outcomes on the list can occur. Finally, the 52 outcomes are equally likely since they are all of the same size, shape, and weight, and a random selection from a fully shuffled deck would favor no one outcome in particular.

2.32 <u>Electric Motor Example</u>. Assume that a shipment of 200 motors, identical in appearance, has arrived, and that, in the unloading process, they are completely mixed up and scattered at random around the supply room. We are then told that 50 of these motors have a defective starter. An experiment consists of selecting one motor at random and checking the starter. Conceptually, the experiment can generate any one of 200 outcomes (any one of the 200 motors can be selected). These 200 outcomes are mutually exclusive since once a given motor is selected, none of the others can be selected. Moreover, these outcomes are equally likely since the haphazard unloading makes no particular motor any more likely to be selected than the others.

2.4   EMPIRICAL EXPERIMENTS

Empirical experiments possess the following attributes:

(a) It is possible to draw up a collectively exhaustive list of outcomes before the experiment is performed.

(b) All outcomes on this list are mutually exclusive.

(c) The outcomes in this collectively exhaustive and mutually exclusive list of outcomes are not equally likely. That is, some outcomes are more likely to occur than others.

(d) The experiment has been performed under identical conditions a great many times, and a record of the results of these experiments is available. Hence, the relative frequency of each outcome is known (i.e., the percentage of the time that each outcome has occurred is known).

The following two examples illustrate these attributes.

2.41 Loaded Die Example.   A gambler takes a regular die to an engineer and asks him to weight it so that the number 6 will be more likely to occur than any of the other numbers. After the die has been "loaded" in this way, the gambler tosses the die 1000 times in exactly the same fashion on a felt-covered surface.   The numbers 1,2,...,6 make up a list of six collectively exhaustive and mutually exclusive outcomes (only these numbers can occur in an experiment, and if, say, the number 6 occurs this precludes the occurrence of any of the other numbers).   Because of the way the die was physically modified, the number 6 is more likely to occur than the others.   Finally, the experiment of tossing the die was performed 1000 times under identical conditions.

2.42 Product Demand Example.   From historical records, a firm knows that 20 percent of the time two units of its product are demanded daily, that 50 percent of the time three units are demanded daily, and that 30 percent of the time four units are demanded daily. The firm is unable to uncover a specific factor to account for this variation. Hence, we can consider the number to be determined stochastically. An experiment consists of examining the sales record after closing time on a given day. The outcomes "2 units demanded", "3 units demanded", and "4 units demanded" make up a collectively exhaustive and mutually exclusive list of outcomes for this experiment. The different relative frequencies observed for each outcome imply that the outcomes are not equally likely to occur; even if these relative frequencies were not known, there still would be no logical reason to suppose that the three outcomes are equally likely. Finally, the fact that relative frequencies are available over a long period of time demonstrates that the experiment has been performed a great many times.

2.5 SUBJECTIVE EXPERIMENTS

Subjective experiments possess the following attributes:

(a) It is possible to draw up a collectively exhaustive list of outcomes before the experiment is performed.
(b) All outcomes on the list are mutually exclusive.
(c) The outcomes in this collectively exhaustive and mutually exclusive list of outcomes are not equally likely.
(d) The experiment has never been performed before.
(e) The person(s) performing the experiment has (have) had considerable experience with similar experiments.

For example, assume a firm is entering a new geographical marketing area. Over the years it has been expanding its business by entering new areas such as this one. Therefore, although no two geographical areas are identical with respect to market potential (point d, above) , the firm does have considerable experience in this sort of venture (point e, above). After the first year the firm performs an experiment by examining its sales records. It can draw up the collectively exhaustive, mutually exclusive, and not equally likely list of four outcomes shown in Table 2.1.

TABLE 2.1

LIST OF OUTCOMES FOR
A SUBJECTIVE EXPERIMENT

Outcome Number	Outcome Description
1	First year sales are under $5,000
2	First year sales are at least $5,000 but under $10,000
3	First year sales are at least $10,000 but under $15,000
4	First year sales are $15,000 or more

We repeat, for emphasis, that the three types of experiments described in this and the two preceding sections, as well as all experiments described in this book, are to be considered stochastic experiments, even though this may not be explicitly spelled out in the discussion. For example, in the preceding illustration, it is assumed that the firm, in drawing up its list of outcomes, feels that the actual outcome which is observed when the experiment is performed, i.e., when the sales record is examined at the end of the year, will be determined by chance or stochastic factors over which it has no control.

In the next three sections, we shall present definitions of probability applicable to the three types of experiments just described. To make clear the type of experiment to which they correspond, we shall call them definitions of a priori probability, empirical probability, and subjective probability. The reader should keep the attributes of each type of experiment clearly before him as he works through these coming sections.

2.6   A PRIORI PROBABILITY

In problems involving uncertainty, interest centers around the probability of a particular event occurring. If an a priori experiment generates the event, then the a priori probability definition must be applied in order to determine the probability of the event.

> Definition 2.1: The a priori probability of an event occurring is the ratio of (a) the number of outcomes in the experiment possessing the distinguishing feature uniquely connected with the event in question, to (b) the number of collectively exhaustive and mutually exclusive outcomes possible in the experiment.

The examples introduced in Section 2.3 will be continued, below, and two additional ones will be introduced in order to illustrate this fundamental definition.

2.61   Card Example.   A card is drawn from a shuffled deck of ordinary playing cards. What is the probability that the event "a heart" will occur? Employing the preceding definition, the answer is 13/52 = 1/4 = .25, since there are 13 outcomes possessing the distinguishing feature connected with the event "a heart" (13 of the cards are hearts), and since there are 52 collectively exhaustive and mutually exclusive outcomes possible.

Similarly, the reader should be able to readily verify that the probability of "a queen" is 4/52 = 1/13 = .077, the probability of "a queen or king" is 8/52 = 2/13 = .154, and the probability of the event "a number between two and five, including 2 and 5" is 16/52 = 4/13 = .308.

Note, for example, that the probability (.154) of the event "a queen or king" is twice as great as the probability (.077) of the event "a queen" (.154/.077 = 2). As this implies, the former event is twice as likely as the latter. This implication is also intuitively evident, since twice as many outcomes are associated with the former event as with the latter event.

2.62   Electric Motor Example.   A shipment of 200 apparently identical electric motors has arrived, 50 of which are known to have defective starters. In the process of being unloaded, all 200 motors are scattered at random around the supply room.   If a motor is selected and its starter checked, what is the probability of the event "a defective starter" occurring? Employing the definition given earlier, the answer is 50/200 = 1/4 = .25, since 50 outcomes possess the distinguishing feature associated with the event "a defective starter", and since the number of collectively exhaustive and mutually exclusive outcomes is 200.

Similarly, the probability of the event "a nondefective starter" is 150/200 = 3/4 = .75. Note that the probability (.75) of the event "a nondefective starter" is three times as likely as the event "a defective starter".

2.63   Die Example.   Assume a single ordinary unbiased die is tossed and the number of dots on the upturned face recorded.   The numbers 1,2,...,6 make up a collectively exhaustive and mutually exhaustive list of six outcomes (why?), and these outcomes are equally likely (since the die is unbiased or identically weighted on all six surfaces). Since this experiment possesses the three attributes specified at the beginning of Section 2.3, we know this is an a priori experiment. Hence, the probability of any event generated by this experiment can be determined by utilizing the definition given at the beginning of this section.

What is the probability of the event "a three-spot"? Since only one outcome has the distinguishing feature associated with this event, and since there are six outcomes possible in the experiment, the answer is 1/6 = .167.

What is the probability of the event "four or less spots"? Four outcomes possess the property of having four or less spots (viz., the four surfaces bearing 1,2,3, and 4 spots, respectively). Hence, the desired probability is 4/6 = 2/3 = .667.

2.64   Coin Example.   An experiment consists of tossing two fair coins (i.e., coins whose two sides are weighted equally) into the air simultaneously, and observing the head-tail pattern on the upturned sides. Assume that one coin is a penny

and the other a dime. The upturned side on the penny could be
a head (denoted by $\underline{H}_P$, while the upturned side of the dime
could be a head (denoted by $\underline{H}_D$) or a tail (denoted by $\underline{T}_D$). We
can represent these two possible patterns by the symbols
$\underline{H}_P\underline{H}_D$ and $\underline{H}_P\underline{T}_D$, respectively. On the other hand, the upturned side on the penny could have been a tail (denoted by $\underline{T}_P$).
In this case, the two possible resulting patterns can be repre-
sented by $\underline{T}_P\underline{H}_D$ and $\underline{T}_P\underline{T}_D$. Altogether, then, the possible
outcomes of this experiment are the four configurations

$$\underline{H}_P\underline{H}_D, \ \underline{H}_P\underline{T}_D, \ \underline{T}_P\underline{H}_D, \ \underline{T}_P\underline{T}_D \qquad (2.1)$$

These outcomes are collectively exhaustive and mutually
exclusive (why?). Moreover, since the coins are fair, no one
side is more likely to turn up than another, and, thus, the four
outcomes specified above are equally likely. Hence, we have
constructed an a priori experiment.
    What is the probability of the event "exactly one head"
being generated by this experiment? We see from the list of
outcomes specified by List 2.1 that two outcomes (viz., $\underline{H}_P\underline{T}_D$
and $\underline{T}_P\underline{H}_D$) represent exactly one head. Hence the probability of the desired event is $2/4 = 1/2 = .5$.
    What is the probability of the event "at least one head"?
Again from List 2.1, we see that three outcomes (viz., $\underline{H}_P\underline{H}_D$,
$\underline{H}_P\underline{T}_D$, $\underline{T}_P\underline{H}_D$) indicate the occurrence of at least one (i.e.,
one or two) heads. Thus, the probability requested is
$3/4 = .75$.
    The reader should be able to verify that the probability
of the event "exactly two heads" is $1/4 = .25$. Moreover, the
probability of the event "two or more heads" is also $1/4 = .25$
(why?).

<u>2.65 Impossible Events</u>.   In the preceding coin example,
what is the probability of the event "exactly three heads"?
Employing the a priori probability definition, the answer is
obtained by calculating the ratio of (a),the number of outcomes in the experiment possessing this characteristic (for

this event the number is 0) to (b), the total number of collectively exhaustive and mutually exclusive outcomes (for this
experiment this number is 4), i.e., 0/4 = 0.

In the die example above (Section 2.63) what is the probability of the event "an eight-spot" occurring on the toss of the
single die? Since none of the outcomes on the list of six possible outcomes possess this characteristic, the probability is
0/6 = 0. In the electric motor example (Section 2.62), what is
the probability of the event "a defective and a nondefective
starter" occurring when a single motor is selected at random? Since each motor possesses just one starter, and since
it is either defective or not defective, none of the 200 possible
outcomes (none of the 200 possible motors which could be selected) will possess this characteristic; hence, again the probability of this event is 0/200 = 0. Finally, in the card example (Section 2.61), what is the probability that the event "a
sixteen of diamonds" will occur when a single card is selected
from a shuffled deck of 52 ordinary playing cards? Since
none of the 52 possible outcomes of the experiment possess
this feature, the probability is, as in the other examples,
0/52 = 0.

All the events described in the two preceding paragraphs
had a probability of 0. Moreover, they all are impossible.
That is, the nature of the experiment is such that these events
cannot possibly occur. Hence, we conclude that the a priori
probability definition has the property that the probability of
an impossible event is 0.

2.66 Certain Events.   In the coin example of the preceding
section, what is the probability of the event "two or fewer
heads"? All of the possible outcomes possess this characteristic: from List 2.1, the first outcome shows exactly two
heads, the second and third show 1 head each (which is less
than 2 heads), and the fourth outcome shows 0 heads.
Hence, employing the probability definition, the probability
sought is 4/4 = 1.

Similarly, in the die example (Section 2.63), the probability of the event "the number of spots is between 1 and 6
inclusive" is 6/6 = 1, since all of the possible outcomes will
show either 1,2,..., or 6 spots. Finally, the reader can verify
that in the electric motor example (Section 2.62) the probability

of the event "a defective or a nondefective starter" is
200/200 = 1, and in the card example (Section 2.61) the probability of the event "a club, diamond, heart or spade" is
52/52 = 1.

All of the events described in the two preceding paragraphs had a probability of 1. Furthermore, they all represented events which were absolutely certain to occur in the
experiments in question. As these results demonstrate, a
further property of a priori probabilities is that the probability of certain events is 1.

2.67   Range of A Priori Probabilities.   All of the probabilities computed so far have ranged between 0 and 1 inclusive.
We shall now show that this is no coincidence.

The ratio given in the probability definition can never be
negative, since the list of possible outcomes in an experiment
either contains one or more outcomes with a certain characteristic or it does not contain any such outcomes. A negative
number of outcomes simply has no meaning in this context.
Hence, 0 is the lowest value the probability of any event can
take.

Moreover, the number of outcomes possessing a given
characteristic can never exceed the total number of outcomes
possible in the experiment. This means the numerator of the
probability ratio can never exceed the denominator, and, thus,
the probability ratio can never exceed 1. That is, 1 is the
highest value the probability of any event can assume.

2.68   Interpretation of A Priori Probabilities.   We know that
impossible events have a probability of 0 and that certain
events have a probability of 1. Uncertain but not impossible
events, i.e., events that may or may not occur in any one experiment, therefore have a probability (denoted by P) in the
range $0 < P < 1$. It should be evident to the reader that the
closer the probability of an event is to 1, the more likely it is
to occur. This follows because the closer the probability is
to 1, the greater is the relative number of outcomes in the experiment possessing the characteristic associated with the
event, and, hence, the greater the chance of one of these outcomes (and therefore the event) being observed. The same

reasoning indicates that the closer the probability of an event is to 0, the less likely is the event to occur.

Thus the a priori probability definition yields a scale on which we can place all events defined in a priori experiments. This scale enables us to immediately rank the likelihoods of all events. Moreover, it indicates the degree to which any one event is more (less) likely than any of the others.

Figure 2.1 shows such a probability scale for the events "a king of diamonds", "a queen", "a king or queen", "a spade", and "a spade or heart or diamond" which might be generated by an experiment in which a single card is drawn from a shuffled deck of playing cards. The reader can place other events on this scale (e.g., the probability of the event "a picture card"). In the Exercises for this section the reader will be asked to construct probability scales for events generated by other experiments.

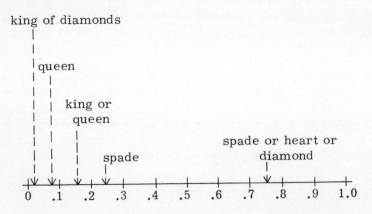

Figure 2.1. Probability scale for card experiment

Before concluding our discussion of a priori probabilities, we should make the following point. If the probability of an event, say, the drawing of a heart from a deck of playing cards, is calculated as 1/4 = .25, this does not mean that a heart will be observed on every fourth draw. Rather, it means that if the experiment is performed a great many times, the long-run ratio, of the number of hearts observed to the number of experiments, will approach and eventually settle on the value .25. All the probabilities that we discuss in this book should be interpreted in this way. Table 2.2 illustrates this point for the experiment just described. As the table shows, the experiment was performed 400 times and the probability ratio calculated after the 4th, 40th, 80th, etc., experiments.

TABLE 2.2

PROBABILITY RATIOS FOR THE EVENT "A HEART"
IN CARD EXPERIMENT N = 4,40,80,...,400

Number of Experiments $\underline{N}$	Number of Experiments in which A Heart Occurred $\underline{n}$	$\underline{n}/\underline{N}$
4	0	0
40	5	.125
80	15	.188
120	25	.208
160	44	.275
200	48	.240
300	76	.253
400	100	.250

2.7   EMPIRICAL PROBABILITY

Now that we have defined and illustrated a priori probability, we turn our attention to what we shall call empirical probability. If an empirical experiment generates an event, then the empirical probability definition must be applied in order to determine the probability of the event. In applying this definition, the reader should recall (from the beginning of Section 2.4) that one of the attributes of empirical experiments is that the experiment has been performed many times under identical conditions, so that the relative frequency of each outcome can be meaningfully computed.

Definition 2.2: The empirical probability of an event occurring is the ratio of (a) the number of experiments in which the event has occurred to (b) the total number of experiments performed.

The careful reader will note that as the number of experiments increases, the ratio specified in Definition 2.2 may fluctuate. We shall now illustrate this point.

2.71   The Large Number of Experiments Condition.   In the example of Section 2.42, a firm has recorded, over a period of time, the number of days in which a specified number of units of its product was demanded. For instance, it is given that 20 percent of the time 2 units of the product were demanded daily. We regard each recording of the number of units demanded daily as an empirical experiment.
    Table 2.3 shows how the ratio

$$\frac{\text{number of days in which daily demand was 2 units}}{\text{Total number of days product was offered for sale}} = \frac{D_2}{N}$$

has fluctuated over time. We see that as the number of experiments N (the number of days the product is offered for sale) increases from 10 to 400, the ratio D_2/N tends to fluctuate around the value .2, the difference between the ratio and .2 narrowing as N increases. After 350 experiments have been performed, the ratio finally centers on the value .2.
    The correct interpretation of Definition 2.2, then, is that empirical probabilities are meaningful only after a large number of experiments have been performed. As the number of experiments increases, the probability ratio computed approaches the true underlying ratio more and more closely. Hence, whenever we employ empirical probabilities, we may be employing approximations to the true probabilities of the events in question. However, if the number of experiments

upon which the probability calculation is based is large, we
can be assured that the computed ratio is not significantly
different from the true ratio.

TABLE 2.3

PROBABILITY RATIO FOR THE EVENT "2 UNITS
DEMANDED DAILY" FOR $\underline{N}$ = 10,50,...,400

Number of Days Product Offered for Sale $\underline{N}$	Number of Days 2 Units Demanded $\underline{D}_2$	Probability of Event "2 Units Demanded Daily" $\underline{D}_2/\underline{N}$
10	3	.30
50	8	.16
100	24	.24
150	35	.23
200	36	.18
250	48	.19
300	63	.21
350	70	.20
400	80	.20

How do we determine what is a sufficiently large number
of experiments? A good deal of experience with the data and
probability calculations in question may provide a person with
sufficient confidence to arbitrarily say a particular $\underline{N}$ (i.e.,
number of experiments) is "large enough".

A more objective procedure would be to compute the probability ratio(s) for the event(s) in question for increasing values of $\underline{N}$, as we did in Table 2.3, and determine whether a sufficient number of experiments has been performed for the
ratio to level off and center on a fixed value. Table 2.3 indicated that for the product demand example, 350 experiments
was a sufficient number.

If, for the largest available value of $\underline{N}$, the ratio has not
yet completely stabilized, the pattern of fluctuation should indicate the central tendency toward which the ratio is gravi-
tating. For example, in Table 2.3 after 300 experiments the
ratio has not completely settled down, yet it is apparent that

it is converging on a value very close to .2. Figure 2.2, which is a graph of Table 2.3, makes this tendency all the more evident.

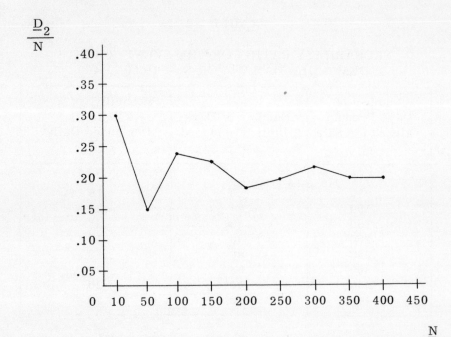

$$\frac{D_2}{N}$$

Figure 2.2. Probability ratio for the event "2 units demanded daily" for $\underline{N}$ = 10,50,...,400

What if the results of only a few experiments are available? In this case, Definition 2.2 can be applied only with caution, if at all. The probability ratio computed from any number of experiments is only an approximation to the true probability, and the approximation determined from a relatively few experiments may be sufficiently far from the mark to invalidate conclusions drawn from the probability analysis of the given problem.

The preceding discussion has assumed that the probability ratio will stabilize around a fixed value as the number of experiments is increased. A good deal of evidence gathered by many people over a long period of time substantiates this

assumption when all of the conditions of empirical experiments are satisfied. If, when a table such as Table 2.3 is
prepared, the probability ratio fluctuates widely over all val-
ues of $\underline{N}$ ($\underline{N}$ is large) and shows no tendency towards stabil-
ization, the reason is very likely that all the experiments
were not performed under identical conditions. For example,
in the illustration of Table 2.3, if seasonal influences were
present in the data, it is not likely that the pattern actually
pictured would emerge. This is because some experiments
would have been performed in winter time and others in the
summer, and variations in the demand for a seasonal product
(e.g., ice cream) would reflect this difference in underlying
conditions.

2.72   Further Examples.   The student should review the
example introduced in Section 2.42. We described a situation
in which a firm knows that 20 percent of the time two units
of its product are demanded daily, 50 percent of the time three
units are demanded daily, and 30 percent of the time four units
are demanded daily. Assuming that a sufficiently large number of experiments have been performed in obtaining these
ratios, we can say that the probabilities of the events "2,3, and
4 units demanded daily" are .2, .5, and .3, respectively.

In Section 2.41 we presented an example in which an engineer physically modified a die so that the number 6 would
turn up more often than any of the others. An experiment
consists of tossing the die and observing the number on the
upturned face. To determine the probabilities of the events
"a 1,2,3,4,5, and 6 on the upturned face", a gambler tosses the
die 1,000 times (performs 1,000 experiments) and records the
results in Table 2.4. Employing the empirical probability
definition (i.e., Definition 2.2) it appears that the probabilities
of the events just specified are, respectively, .05, .10, .20,
.17, .08, and .40.

2.73   Simple and Multiple Events.   The reader will recall
that for all types of experiments (i.e., a priori, empirical, and
subjective), we have described the possible outcomes in such a
way as to assure that they will make up a collectively exhaustive and mutually exclusive list. Further, we have defined an

TABLE 2.4

PROBABILITY RATIOS FOR SIMPLE EVENTS
IN LOADED DIE EXPERIMENT (N = 100,200,...,1,000)

Number of Times Die Tossed N	Number of Times the Upturned Face Showed the Number						Probability Ratios					
	1 n_1	2 n_2	3 n_3	4 n_4	5 n_5	6 n_6	$\frac{n_1}{N}$	$\frac{n_2}{N}$	$\frac{n_3}{N}$	$\frac{n_4}{N}$	$\frac{n_5}{N}$	$\frac{n_6}{N}$
100	10	5	28	15	6	36	.10	.05	.28	.15	.06	.36
200	16	16	32	38	20	78	.08	.08	.16	.19	.10	.39
300	18	33	66	45	21	117	.06	.11	.22	.15	.07	.39
400	24	36	76	64	40	160	.06	.09	.19	.16	.10	.40
500	25	45	105	85	45	195	.05	.09	.21	.17	.09	.39
600	30	66	114	96	54	240	.05	.11	.19	.16	.09	.40
800	40	80	160	136	64	320	.05	.10	.20	.17	.08	.40
1,000	50	100	200	170	80	400	.05	.10	.20	.17	.08	.40

event as a set of one or more of the outcomes in this list. If an
event contains a single outcome (if only one outcome has the
distinguishing feature associated with the event), then we shall
call this a simple event. If the event contains two or more outcomes, we shall refer to this as a multiple event.[1]

For example, in the a priori experiment involving the
drawing of a single card from a deck of playing cards, the
event "a king of diamonds" is a simple event (only one outcome
possesses this characteristic) while the event "a king" is a
multiple event (four outcomes possess this characteristic).

In the loaded die example described in the preceding section, the events whose probabilities are calculated directly in
Table 2.4 are thus simple events.[2]   Moreover, in the product
demand example also treated in that section, the events "2

---

[1] The reader should not confuse this term with the common meaning of the term "compound event", which will be treated in a later chapter.

[2] Recall that in a priori experiments all outcomes are equally likely, while this is not
necessarily the case in empirical experiments.

units are demanded daily", "3 units are demanded daily", and
"4 units are demanded daily" are also simple events.

While we have automatically employed Definition 2.1 to
calculate the probabilities of both simple and multiple events,
we have used Definition 2.2 to compute only the probabilities
of simple events. However, once the probabilities of the
simple events have been calculated, the probabilities of multiple events can be readily calculated in this case as well, by
direct application of Definition 2.2.

For example, in the loaded die example, the multiple
event "a 1 or 2" contains two mutually exclusive (but not
equally likely) outcomes. From Table 2.4 we know that a 1
is observed in 50, and a 2 in 100, of the experiments, so that
the event "1 or 2" is observed in 150/1,000 = 15 percent of
the experiments. That is, the probability of this multiple
event is .15. Alternatively, instead of utilizing the basic data,
we could add the probabilities of the simple events which make
up the multiple event. That is, if we let $\underline{P}(\underline{E}_1)$ denote the probability of the simple event "a 1", $\underline{P}(\underline{E}_2)$ denote the probability
of the simple event "a 2", and $\underline{P}(\underline{E}_1 \vee \underline{E}_2)$ the probability of
the multiple event "a 1 or 2", we can write

$$\underline{P}(\underline{E}_1 \vee \underline{E}_2) = \underline{P}(\underline{E}_1) + \underline{P}(\underline{E}_2) = .05 + .10 = .15$$

Similarly, the reader can verify that the probability of the
multiple event "a 1,2, or 3" [denoted by $\underline{P}(\underline{E}_1 \vee \underline{E}_2 \vee \underline{E}_3)$] can
be calculated from Definition 2.2

$$\underline{P}(\underline{E}_1 \vee \underline{E}_2 \vee \underline{E}_3) = \frac{50 + 100 + 200}{1,000} = .35$$

or by adding the probabilities of the simple events contained
in the multiple event

$$\underline{P}(\underline{E}_1 \vee \underline{E}_2 \vee \underline{E}_3) = \underline{P}(\underline{E}_1) + \underline{P}(\underline{E}_2) + \underline{P}(\underline{E}_3)$$
$$= .05 + .10 + .20 = .35$$

In the product demand example discussed in the preceding section, the following three simple probabilities were
derived: 1) the probability of the event "demand is 2 units
daily" [denoted by $\underline{P}(\underline{D}_2)$] was .2, 2) the probability of the
event "demand is 3 units daily" [$\underline{P}(\underline{D}_3)$] was .5, and 3) the
probability of the event "demand is 4 units daily" [$\underline{P}(\underline{D}_4)$]
was .3. What is the probability of the multiple event "demand
is 2 or 3 units daily" [$\underline{P}(\underline{D}_2 \vee \underline{D}_3)$]? We know that 20 percent

of the time the demand was for 2 units, 50 percent of the time it was 3 units, and thus that in 20% + 50% = 70% of the experiments it was for either 2 or 3 units. Hence, from Definition 2.2, the probability of the multiple event is .7. We obtain the same answer by adding the probabilities of the two simple events contained in this multiple event, i.e.,

$$\underline{P}(\underline{D_2} \lor \underline{D_3}) = \underline{P}(\underline{D_2}) + \underline{P}(\underline{D_3}) = .2 + .5 = .7$$

Typically, this latter approach is the one employed.

The validity of summing the probabilities of simple events to obtain the probability of the multiple event which includes them can be established as follows. First we take an a priori experiment. Let the set of $\underline{n}$ possible outcomes be denoted by $\underline{x_1}, \underline{x_2}, ..., \underline{x_n}$, and the probabilities of the corresponding simple events by $\underline{P}(\underline{x_1}), \underline{P}(\underline{x_2}), ..., \underline{P}(\underline{x_n})$. Now, from the definition of a priori probability, we have, for example, $\underline{P}(\underline{x_1}) = 1/\underline{n}$, $\underline{P}(\underline{x_2}) = 1/\underline{n}$, and $\underline{P}(\underline{x_1} \lor \underline{x_2}) = 2/n$. But $\underline{P}(\underline{x_1} \lor \underline{x_2}) = 2/n = 1/n + 1/n = \underline{P}(\underline{x_1}) + \underline{P}(\underline{x_2})$. Hence, the probability of the multiple event "$\underline{x_1}$ or $\underline{x_2}$ occurs" equals the sum of the probabilities of the simple events it contains. The reader should now be able to generalize this result to any multiple event in an a priori experiment.

The procedure for establishing this principle in empirical experiments is similar. Let $\underline{x_1}, \underline{x_2}, ..., \underline{x_n}$ denote the $\underline{n}$ possible outcomes of the experiment, and $\underline{P}(\underline{x_1}), \underline{P}(\underline{x_2}), ..., \underline{P}(\underline{x_n})$ the probabilities of the corresponding simple events. Assume that these probabilities were established after $\underline{N}$ experiments were performed. If we let $\underline{n_1}, \underline{n_2}, ..., \underline{n_n}$ denote the number of times each outcome occurred, respectively (note that $\underline{n_1} + \underline{n_2} + ... + \underline{n_n} = \underline{N}$), then we have, for example, $\underline{P}(\underline{x_1}) = \underline{n_1}/\underline{N}$, $\underline{P}(\underline{x_2}) = \underline{n_2}/\underline{N}$, and $\underline{P}(\underline{x_1} \lor \underline{x_2}) = (\underline{n_1} + \underline{n_2})/\underline{N}$. But

$$\underline{P}(\underline{x_1} \lor \underline{x_2}) = (\underline{n_1} + \underline{n_2})/\underline{N} = (\underline{n_1}/\underline{N}) + (\underline{n_2}/\underline{N}) = \underline{P}(\underline{x_1}) + \underline{P}(\underline{x_2})$$

as in the a priori case.

By a similar analysis, we can also verify the property that, in both a priori and empirical experiments, the sum of the probabilities of all simple events is 1. For example, in the a priori case we have

$$\underline{P}(\underline{x}_1) + \underline{P}(\underline{x}_2) + \ldots + \underline{P}(\underline{x}_n) = (1/\underline{n}) + (1/\underline{n}) + \ldots$$
$$+ (1/\underline{n}) = \underline{n}/\underline{n} = 1$$

and in the empirical case we have

$$\underline{P}(\underline{x}_1) + \underline{P}(\underline{x}_2) + \ldots + \underline{P}(\underline{x}_n) = (\underline{n}_1/\underline{N}) + (\underline{n}_2/\underline{N}) + \ldots$$
$$+ (\underline{n}_n/\underline{N}) = \underline{N}/\underline{N} = 1$$

2.74 Impossible and Certain Events.   In the loaded die example (Table 2.4) what is the probability of the event "a 7"? This event occurred 0 times in 1,000 experiments so that, from Definition 2.2, its probability is 0/1,000 = 0. In the demand for a product example, what is the probability of the event "10 units are demanded daily"? Since this event oc-curred 0 times in a great many experiments, its probability is 0 also. Note that both of these events are impossible in the experiments defined. Thus, as with a priori probabilities, the empirical probability of an impossible event is 0.

In the loaded die example, what is the probability of the event "a number equal to 6 or less"? This event occurred 1,000 times in 1,000 trials (Table 2.4), and hence, from Def-inition 2.2, its probability is 1. Similarly, in the demand for a product example, the event "daily demand is between 2 and 4 units inclusive" occurred 100 percent of the time, so that its probability is also 1. Both of the events just described are certain events. Again, as with a priori probabilities, the empirical probability of a certain event is 1.

2.75 Range and Interpretation of Empirical Probabilities. All the probabilities calculated in Section 2.7 have ranged between 0 and 1. These values define the upper and lower limits of empirical probabilities. This is so because we see, from Definition 2.2, that negative values are impossible (it makes no sense to talk about an event occurring a negative number of times in $\underline{N}$ experiments), as are values greater than 1 (it is impossible for an event to occur more than $\underline{N}$ times in exactly $\underline{N}$ trials).

Thus we see that empirical probabilities have the same range as a priori probabilities. They also are interpreted in the same way. The closer the probability of an event is to 0, the less likely it is to occur, and the closer to 1, the more likely. This relationship should be readily apparent, since the closer a probability is to 0, the smaller is the relative frequency with which it has occurred in the past, and, under identical conditions, the smaller the likelihood of its occurring on the next experiment. The reverse argument holds for probabilities closer to 1.

Thus a probability scale can be constructed for empirical probabilities which would be identical to the one constructed for a priori probabilities (Fig. 2.1). The probabilities of all events definable for a given empirical experiment could be placed on such a scale, and the rank and precise relationship of any one probability to the others made readily evident. The reader will be asked to construct such scales in the Exercise section at the end of this chapter.

2.8   SUBJECTIVE PROBABILITY

Before continuing, the reader should review Section 2.5 to be certain he remembers the attributes and interpretations of subjective experiments. If we are interested in the probability of an event that might be generated by a subjective experiment, we must apply the subjective probability definition.

Definition 2.3: The subjective probability of a simple event is a number between 0 and 1 which is arbitrarily assigned by a person(s) who has (have) some experience with similar experiments. The more likely the event is considered to be, the closer the number should be to 1; the less likely, the closer to 0. This number should be assigned at the same time that other such numbers are assigned to the other outcomes in the list of collectively exhaustive and mutually exclusive outcomes. The sum of all these assigned numbers must be exactly 1. The probabilities of multiple events are determined by summing the probabilities of all simple events included in the

multiple event. Impossible and certain events have
probabilities of 0 and 1, respectively.

2.81 Interpretation of Subjective Probabilities.   A careful
reading of the preceding definition will indicate that subjective
probabilities are defined so that they have the same range and
can be interpreted in exactly the same fashion as a priori and
empirical probabilities. Subjective probabilities, on the other
hand, cannot be determined objectively from the logic of an
experiment (as in a priori experiments) or from empirical
data (as in empirical experiments). Rather, they are employed
when such objective evidence is absent, but when persons with
some experience (and, perhaps, intuition) are available.

   For this reason, decisions made on the basis of subjective
probability analysis may be more open to question than those
based on the more objective probability calculations. However,
when it is impossible to perform a priori or empirical experiments, subjective probabilities may provide a next-best line
of attack. They force the decision makers to explicitly state
their assessments of the likelihood of the various outcomes.
In this way the entire decision-making process is facilitated,
since, if significantly different assessments emerge from the
different people involved with the decision, each person will
be forced to spell out his assumptions and defend his foregone
conclusions. Thus the subjective probability determination
provides a meaningful frame of reference for the utilization of
the experience possessed by the different people involved.
Once the subjective probabilities have been agreed upon, they
can then be used in a straightforward solution of the problem
(as will be demonstrated in later chapters). In this way, it is
possible to take an essentially subjective decision situation
and quantify it in a manner that very likely will improve the
decision that might otherwise have been made.

2.82   Marketing Example.   In Section 2.5, we describe a
subjective experiment in which a firm was about to enter a new
geographical marketing area. The reader can refer to this
section for more details, but Table 2.1 was drawn up to show
a list of four collectively exhaustive and mutually exclusive
outcomes. This table, together with a corresponding set of

subjective probabilities agreed upon by the marketing department, is presented in Table 2.5.

TABLE 2.5

PROBABILITIES OF SIMPLE EVENTS
FOR MARKETING EXAMPLE

Outcome Number	Outcome Description	Subjective Probability
1	First year sales are under $5,000	.3
2	First year sales are at least $5,000 but under $10,000	.4
3	First year sales are at least $10,000 but under $15,000	.2
4	First year sales are $15,000 or more	.1
		1.0

For example, the probability of the simple event "first year sales are under $5,000" is seen to be .3. Note that the probabilities included in this collectively exhaustive and mutually exclusive set of outcomes sum to 1. What is the probability of the multiple event "sales are at least $5,000 but under $15,000"? Adding the probabilities of the two outcomes (viz., outcomes 1 and 2) included in this event, we obtain .4 + .2 = .6 as the required probability.

2.9   APPLYING THE RELEVANT PROBABILITY DEFINITION

We have described three types of experiments, viz., a priori, empirical, and subjective, by indicating the attributes associated with each. On the basis of these three sets of attributes, three probability definitions were formulated. Numerous examples served to indicate the implications and interpretations of these definitions.

In each of the three cases, probability was shown to be a numerical measure (called the probability ratio) of the likelihood of a particular event. This measure, in each case, ranges between 0 and 1. The higher is this measure, the more likely is the event.

In applying these definitions, the reader must first properly identify the relevant experiment as a priori, empirical or subjective. In all three types of experiments, we assume that, as a first step, it is possible to draw up a list of collectively exhaustive and mutually exclusive outcomes. Second, a determination must be made as to whether these outcomes are equally likely. If they are, then the a priori probability definition is applicable. If these outcomes are not equally likely, but if a large number of experiments have, or can be, performed under identical conditions, then the empirical probability definition is the one to use. If these outcomes are not equally likely and if a large number of experiments have not been (and cannot be) performed, then, if there are available people who have had considerable experience with similar experiments, the subjective probability definition can be employed. Finally, in the last case cited, if nobody is available with qualified experience, then probability analysis cannot be meaningfully applied as an aid to decision-making under uncertainty.

2.10   DISCUSSION AND REVIEW QUESTIONS

1. Distinguish between the attributes of a priori, empirical, and subjective experiments.

2. Give examples, different from those given in the text, of a priori, empirical, and subjective experiments.

3. Define collectively exhaustive, mutually exclusive, and equally likely.

4. The probability of obtaining the event "a head" when a fair coin is tossed is $1/2 = .5$. Yet, in six tosses of the coin, the event "a tail" turned up each time. Are these results inconsistent with the probability given the event "a head"?

5. In empirical experiments, how do you know when a sufficiently large number of experiments has been performed?

6. Distinguish between simple and multiple events. Give examples of each.

7. In calculating the probability of a given event, how do you determine which probability definition is applicable?

2.11   EXERCISES

1. An experiment consists of tossing a pair of unbiased dice and observing the sum of the spots on the two upturned faces.

    (a) What kind of experiment is this? Why?

    (b) Draw up a list of collectively exhaustive and mutually exclusive outcomes. How many outcomes are in this list? (Ans.: 36)

    (c) What is the probability of the event:
       (1) the sum of the spots is 2? (Ans.: 1/36)
       (2) the sum of the spots is 7? (Ans.: 1/6)
       (3) the sum of the spots is 11? (Ans.: 1/18)
       (4) the sum of the spots is 7 or 11?
       (5) the sum of the spots is less than 8?

    (d) Place the preceding events on a probability scale.

2. An experiment consists of tossing three coins simultaneously and observing the resulting head-tail pattern.

    (a) What kind of experiment is this? Why?

    (b) Draw up a list of collectively exhaustive and mutually exclusive outcomes.

    (c) What is the probability of the event:
       (1) 0 heads appear?
       (2) 1 head appears?
       (3) 2 heads appear?
       (4) 2 or more heads appear?
       (5) 2 or fewer heads appear?
       (6) 4 heads appear?

    (d) Place the preceding events on a probability scale.

3. After a worker has become thoroughly familiar with a particular operation, a time-study man times this worker on this operation 100 times. The results are shown in Table 2.6.

The time study man feels that chance alone accounts for the varying times observed.

TABLE 2.6

RESULTS OF TIME STUDY

Number of Minutes Required to Complete Operation	Number of Times Stated Number Minutes Required
2	5
3	15
4	30
5	28
6	22
	100

(a) What kind of experiment is this? Why?

(b) What is the probability that, in order to complete the operation, the worker will require:
 (1) 2 minutes?
 (2) 2 or 3 minutes?
 (3) 3 or less minutes?
 (4) more than 3 minutes? (Ans.: .8)
 (5) 10 minutes?

(c) Place these events on a probability scale.

4. An attempt is being made to unionize a plant. Table 2.7 shows the results of a poll taken among the 100 employees in the plant.

(a) If a worker is selected at random, what is the probability that he will:
 (1) favor union affiliation? (Ans.: .7)
 (2) neither favor nor oppose union affiliation?
 (3) be a clerical worker?
 (4) be a clerical or supervisory worker? (Ans.: .3)
 (5) be a production worker who favors affiliation?
 (6) be a supervisory worker who favors affiliation? (Ans.: .01)
 (7) be a supervisory worker with no opinion?

(b) Place these events on a probability scale?
(c) What kind of experiment is this?   Why?

TABLE 2.7

RESULTS OF POLL

| Worker Category | Union Affiliation | | | |
	Favored	Opposed	No Opinion	Total
Clerical	5	9	6	20
Maintenance	8	1	1	10
Production	56	1	3	60
Supervisory	1	9	0	10
Total	70	20	10	100

3 ▶ RANDOM VARIABLES

3.1 MOTIVATION

Now that we have defined probability, we turn to a discussion of three companion concepts: random variable, probability distribution, and expected value. These additional concepts from the theory of probability are essential to our development of solutions to problems of uncertainty in business decision-making.

In this chapter (and in the remainder of the book), when we speak of the set of outcomes of an experiment, it is to be assumed that the outcomes in this set are collectively exhaustive and mutually exclusive.

3.2 RANDOM VARIABLE

A random variable is not a variable in the usual sense of the word. That is, it is not a quantity that takes on different values. Rather, convention has assigned the following special meaning to the term "random variable".

Definition 3.1: A random variable is a relationship between the set of outcomes of an experiment

> and a set of numbers. This relationship is defined so that to each outcome there corresponds just one number (although different outcomes may correspond to the same number).

In the preceding definition, it is assumed that the set (i.e., list, group, collection) of outcomes is a collectively exhaustive and mutually exclusive set, and that the experiment is a stochastic experiment (as are all experiments described in this book). Moreover, the set of numbers is referred to as the set of values of the random variable so that any one number is a value of the random variable. Thus, while the term "random variable" denotes a specific kind of relationship, the term "value of a random variable" denotes a quantity which takes on different values (a "variable" in the usual sense).

The following examples will clarify this definition.

3.21   Die Example.   An experiment consists of tossing a single unbiased die and observing the number on the upturned face. This is an a priori experiment, and the set of possible outcomes contains the numbers 1, 2, 3, . . . ,6.

Let V denote the random variable (the relationship between the set of outcomes and a set of numbers) whose value for any outcome is 5 if the outcome is odd, and 10 if the outcome is even. Let x denote the outcome of the experiment and $V(x)$ the value of the random variable V when the outcome is x.

Table 3.1 shows this random variable. For example, we see that for $x = 2$, $V(x) = V(2) = 10$. In fact, since $V(2) = V(4) = V(6) = 10$ and $V(1) = V(3) = V(5) = 5$, we see that different outcomes can generate the same value for the random variable, depending on how the random variable is defined. However, each x corresponds to just a single value for the random variable.

It is important to note that more than one random variable can be defined for the same set of outcomes from an experiment. For example, if we let W denote the random variable whose value for any outcome (i.e., any x) is 2 times the outcome $[V(x) = 2x]$, we obtain Table 3.2.

TABLE 3.1

RANDOM VARIABLE $\underline{V}$
DEFINED FOR DIE EXPERIMENT

Outcome of Experiment $\underline{x}$	Value of Random Variable $\underline{V}(\underline{x}) = \begin{cases} 5 & \text{if } \underline{x} \text{ is odd} \\ 10 & \text{if } \underline{x} \text{ is even} \end{cases}$
1	5
2	10
3	5
4	10
5	5
6	10

TABLE 3.2

RANDOM VARIABLE $\underline{W}$
DEFINED FOR DIE EXPERIMENT

Outcome of Experiment $\underline{x}$	Value of Random Variable $W(\underline{x}) = 2\underline{x}$
1	2
2	4
3	6
4	8
5	10
6	12

3.22 Coin Example. An a priori experiment consists of tossing two "fair" coins simultaneously and observing the head-tail pattern on the upturned faces. One coin is a penny and the other a dime. The set of possible outcomes for this experiment is given below:

$$\underline{H}_{\underline{P}}\underline{H}_{\underline{D}}, \quad \underline{H}_{\underline{P}}\underline{T}_{\underline{D}}, \quad \underline{T}_{\underline{P}}\underline{H}_{\underline{D}}, \quad \underline{T}_{\underline{P}}\underline{T}_{\underline{D}}$$

The notation is the same as that used before (Section 2.64); e.g., the outcome $\underline{H}_P \underline{T}_D$ denotes "the penny turned up heads and the dime turned up tails".

Let $\underline{V}$ denote the random variable (the relationship) whose value for any outcome is the number of heads observed, let $\underline{x}$ denote the outcome of the experiment, and let $\underline{V}(\underline{x})$ denote the value of the random variable $\underline{V}$ when the outcome is $\underline{x}$. For example, when $\underline{x} = \underline{H}_P \underline{T}_D$, $\underline{V}(\underline{x}) = \underline{V}(\underline{H}_P \underline{T}_D) = 1$. Table 3.3 shows this random variable.

TABLE 3.3

RANDOM VARIABLE $\underline{V}$
DEFINED FOR COIN EXPERIMENT

Outcome of Experiment $\underline{x}$	Value of Random Variable $\underline{V}(\underline{x})$ = number of heads observed
$\underline{H}_P \underline{H}_D$	2
$\underline{H}_P \underline{T}_D$	1
$\underline{T}_P \underline{H}_D$	1
$\underline{T}_P \underline{T}_D$	0

3.23 Product Demand Example.   An empirical experiment consists of examining the sales record at the end of a day and observing the number of units sold. From past experience, it is known that either 2, 3, or 4 units will be the number observed. That is, the set of outcomes for the experiment contains the numbers 2, 3, and 4.

The price of each unit is $5, and the sale of each unit involves a wrapping cost of $2. $\underline{x}$ denotes the outcome of the experiment; $\underline{R}$ denotes the random variable called "revenue", whose value [denoted by $\underline{R}(\underline{x})$] is the gross revenue from this product daily [$\underline{R}(\underline{x}) = 5\underline{x}$]; $\underline{W}$ denotes the random variable "wrapping cost" whose value [denoted by $\underline{W}(\underline{x})$] is the total wrapping cost daily [i.e., $\underline{W}(\underline{x}) = 2\underline{x}$]; and $\underline{A}$ denotes the random variable "adjusted revenue" whose value [denoted by $\underline{A}(\underline{x})$] is the difference between daily gross revenue and wrapping cost [$\underline{A}(\underline{x}) = \underline{R}(\underline{x}) - \underline{W}(\underline{x})$]. Table 3.4 shows these random variables.

TABLE 3.4

RANDOM VARIABLES $\underline{R}$, $\underline{W}$, AND $\underline{A}$
DEFINED IN PRODUCT DEMAND EXAMPLE

Outcome of Experiment $\underline{x}$	Values of Random Variables		
	$\underline{R}(\underline{x}) = 5\underline{x}$	$\underline{W}(\underline{x}) = 2\underline{x}$	$\underline{A}(\underline{x}) =$ $5\underline{x} - 2\underline{x} = 3\underline{x}$
2	10	4	6
3	15	6	9
4	20	8	12

In some experiments (like the preceding one), the set of possible outcomes is itself a set of numbers. In these cases, it is possible to define an identity random variable $\underline{I}$ whose value [$\underline{I}(\underline{x})$] for any outcome $\underline{x}$ is $\underline{x}$ [$\underline{I}(\underline{x}) = \underline{x}$]. For example, in the illustration given in this section, for $\underline{x} = 2,3,4$ we would have $\underline{I}(2) = 2$, $\underline{I}(3) = 3$, and $\underline{I}(4) = 4$.

3.3 PROBABILITY DISTRIBUTION

Once a set of collectively exhaustive and mutually exclusive outcomes has been determined for an experiment and once a random variable has been defined for this set of outcomes, it then may be possible to construct a probability distribution for this random variable. Such a distribution can be defined as follows:

Definition 3.2: A probability distribution is a relationship, between the set of the different possible

values of a random variable and a set of probabilities, which gives the probability of each different possible value of a random variable.

The following examples will clarify this definition.

3.31   Die Example.   Table 3.1 shows the values of the random
variable $\underline{V}$ defined in Section 3.21. The different values in this
set are 5 and 10. Since three of the six possible outcomes in
this a priori experiment will yield the value 5, its probability is
3/6 = .5. Similarly, the probability of the value 10 is 3/6 = .5.

The first part of Table 3.5 shows this probability distribution. The second part of this table shows the probability distribution for the random variable $\underline{W}$, which also was defined in Section 3.21 and Table 3.2. We denote the different possible values
of the random variable by the lower case form of the letter used
to denote the given random variable; e.g., if $\underline{V}$ denotes the random variable, then $\underline{v}$ denotes the different possible values it can
take. In addition, we denote the probability of obtaining the value $\underline{v}$ by $\underline{P}(\underline{v})$.

TABLE 3.5

PROBABILITY DISTRIBUTIONS FOR RANDOM VARIABLES
$\underline{V}$ AND $\underline{W}$ DEFINED IN DIE EXAMPLE

V		W	
Different Possible Values of $\underline{V}$ $\underline{v}$	Probability of $\underline{v}$ $\underline{P}(\underline{v})$	Different Possible Values of $\underline{W}$ $\underline{w}$	Probability of w $\underline{P}(\underline{w})$
5	.5	2	.167
10	.5	4	.167
		6	.167
	1.0	8	.167
		10	.167
		12	.167
			1.002*

*Differs from 1.000 because of rounding errors.

3.32 Coin and Product Demand Examples. Table 3.3 shows the values of the random variable V described in Section 3.22. The set of different possible values contains the numbers 0,1, and 2. The four possible outcomes of this experiment are equally likely, and two of these outcomes correspond to the number 1, one outcome to the number 0, and one to the number 2. Hence, if we denote the different possible values of the random variable V by v (v = 0,1,2), and the probability of v occurring by $P(v)$, then we have $P(0)$ = 1/4 = .25, $P(1)$ = 2/4 = .5, and $P(2)$ = 1/4 = .25. Table 3.6 shows this probability distribution.

TABLE 3.6

PROBABILITY DISTRIBUTION FOR RANDOM VARIABLE V
DEFINED IN COIN EXAMPLE

Different Possible Values of V v	Probability of v $P(v)$
0	.25
1	.50
2	.25
	1.00

TABLE 3.7

PROBABILITY DISTRIBUTIONS FOR RANDOM VARIABLES
$R, W,$ AND A DEFINED IN PRODUCT DEMAND EXAMPLE

R		W		A	
r	$P(r)$	w	$P(w)$	a	$P(a)$
10	.2	4	.2	6	.2
15	.5	6	.5	9	.5
20	.3	8	.3	12	.3
	1.0		1.0		1.0

Table 3.4 shows the values of the three random variables defined in Section 3.23. Assume the probabilities of there being 2,3, and 4 units demanded daily are .2, .5, and .3, respectively. Then, as the reader can easily verify, Table 3.7 shows the probability distributions for these random variables.

As these examples show, probability distributions have the property that the sum of the probabilities of the different possible values of the given random variable is 1. This is so because: 1) each different possible value of the random variable is associated with one or more of the possible outcomes of the experiment; 2) no two values are associated with the same outcome; and 3) every possible outcome is associated with one, and only one, of the different possible values. This means that: 1) each value is associated with either a single simple event or a set of two or more simple events; 2) no two values correspond to the same simple event; and 3) every possible simple event is associated with one, and only one, of the different possible values. Hence, the set of different possible values of the random variable corresponds exactly to the set of simple events in the experiment.

Figure 3.1 schematically depicts this relationship for an experiment having six possible outcomes (denoted by $\underline{x}_1,\ldots,\underline{x}_6$) and a random variable $\underline{V}$ with three different possible values ($\underline{v}_1$, $\underline{v}_2$, $\underline{v}_3$). We see that $\underline{v}_1$ is associated with the two outcomes (and two simple events) $\underline{x}_1$ and $\underline{x}_2$, $\underline{v}_2$ with the single outcome (and single simple event) $\underline{x}_3$, and $\underline{v}_3$ with the three outcomes (and three simple events) $\underline{x}_4$, $\underline{x}_5$, and $\underline{x}_6$. Thus the set of three different possible values of the random variable $\underline{V}$ corresponds exactly to set of six possible outcomes, and therefore the set of six possible simple events, in the experiment.

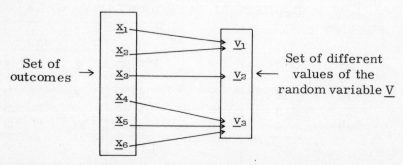

Figure 3.1   Schematic view of a random variable.

From the analysis at the end of Section 2.73, we know that the sum of the probabilities of the simple events in an experiment is 1. Therefore, the sum of the probabilities of the different possible values of the random variable is 1. Exercise 3 in Section 3.7 provides a concrete illustration of this discussion.

3.4   EXPECTED VALUE

Now that we have developed the concepts of a random variable and a probability distribution, we are ready to define another important concept known as the expected value of a random variable.

Definition 3.3: Assume that a random variable V has n different values denoted by v_i ($i = 1, 2, \ldots, n$).

Assume, further, that the probability distribution for V is known, and that the probability of the value v_i is $P(v)_i$. Then the expected value of the random variable V, denoted by $E(V)$, is the quantity

$$E(V) = v_1 P(v_1) + v_2 P(v_2) + \ldots + v_n P(v_n) \quad (3.1)$$

Thus we see that the expected value of a random variable is the sum of the weighted values of the random variable, each value being weighted by its probability of occurrence.

The following examples will show how expected values are calculated in specific cases. A later section will deal explicitly with their interpretation.

3.41   Expected Values of Some Specific Random Variables.

Table 3.5 shows the probability distributions for the random variables V and W defined in the die example. Using Equation 3.1, the expected values of these random variables are calculated as

$$E(V) = v_1 P(v_1) + v_2 P(v_2) = 5 \times .5 + 10 \times .5 = 7.5$$

$$\underline{E(W)} = \underline{w_1}\,\underline{P(w_1}) + \underline{w_2}P(\underline{w_2}) + \underline{w_3}\underline{P}(\underline{w_3}) + \underline{w_4}\,\underline{P(w_4}) + \underline{w_5}\,\underline{P(w_5}))$$

$$+ \underline{w_6}\,\underline{P(w_6}) = 2 \times .167 + 4 \times .167 + 6 \times .167 + 8$$

$$\times .167 + 10 \times .167 + 12 \times .167 = 7$$

Similarly, the expected value of the random variable $\underline{V}$, whose probability distribution is shown in Table 3.6 is

$$\underline{E(V)} = 0 \times .25 + 1 \times .50 + 2 \times .25 = 1$$

and the expected values of the random variables $\underline{R}$, $\underline{W}$ and $\underline{A}$ whose probability distributions are given in Table 3.7 are

$$\underline{E(R)} = 10 \times .2 + 15 \times .5 + 20 \times .3 = 15.5$$

$$\underline{E(W)} = 4 \times .2 + 6 \times .5 + 8 \times .3 = 6.2$$

$$\underline{E(A)} = 6 \times .2 + 9 \times .5 + 12 \times .3 = 9.3$$

3.42 Interpretation of Expected Values. From our definition of probability, we known that the empirical probability of an event can be interpreted as the ratio of (a) the number of times the event actually occurred to (b) the number of experiments actually performed in the long run (when many experiments have been performed). Also, the a priori and subjective probabilities of an event can be interpreted as the ratio of (a) the number of times the event is expected to occur to (b) the number of experiments that might be performed in the long run (when the number of experiments that might be performed is large). Thus if many experiments are actually performed, all three probability definitions imply that the probability of an event is the relative frequency (ratio) of occurrence that will result in this long run.

With this interpretation in mind, it becomes possible to interpret the expected value $\underline{E(V)}$ of the random variable $\underline{V}$ as the value of the random variable that will be observed on the average in the long run. To justify this last statement, consider the value $\underline{v}_i$ ($\underline{i} = 1,2,...,\underline{n}$) of $\underline{V}$ which occurs with probability $\underline{P(v}_i)$. Assume a great many, say $\underline{N}$, experiments are per-formed. Then, according to the preceding long run interpretation of probability, we would expect that the number (denoted by n_i) of times the value $\underline{v}_i$ would occur can be determined from the relationship

$$P(\underline{v}_i) = \frac{\underline{n}_i}{N}$$

or $\quad \underline{n}_i = P(\underline{v}_i)\underline{N}$ $\hspace{4cm}$ (3.2)

The value of $\underline{V}$ on the average per experiment would

be $\quad \dfrac{\underline{v}_1\underline{n}_1 + \underline{v}_2\underline{n}_2 + \ldots + \underline{v}_{\underline{n}}\underline{n}_{\underline{n}}}{\underline{N}}$

Substituting Eq. 3.2 in the preceding expression yields

$$\frac{\underline{v}_1 P(\underline{v}_1)\underline{N} + \underline{v}_2 P(\underline{v}_2)\underline{N} + \ldots + \underline{v}_{\underline{n}} P(\underline{v}_{\underline{n}})\underline{N}}{\underline{N}}$$

$$= \frac{\underline{N}\left[\underline{v}_1 P(\underline{v}_1) + \underline{v}_2 P(\underline{v}_2) + \ldots + \underline{v}_{\underline{n}} P(\underline{v}_{\underline{n}})\right]}{\underline{N}}$$

$$= \underline{v}_1 P(\underline{v}_1) + \underline{v}_2 P(\underline{v}_2) + \ldots + \underline{v}_{\underline{n}} P(\underline{v}_{\underline{n}})$$

But this last expression is identical to the definition of $\underline{E(V)}$ given in Equation 3.1. Hence, the expected value of a random variable can be interpreted as the value of the random variable that will be observed on the average in the long run.

For example, in the coin example summarized in Table 3.6, we found that the expected value of the random variable $\underline{V}$ was $\underline{E(V)} = 1$. This means, if this experiment were performed (the two coins tossed) 1,000 times, the value $\underline{v}_1 = 0$ would be observed about 250 times, the value $\underline{v}_2 = 1$ about 500 times, and the value $\underline{v}_3 = 2$ about 250 times. Hence, the long-run average value per experiment would be

$$\frac{0(250) + 1(500) + 2(250)}{1,000} = 1 = \underline{E(V)}$$

In addition to this long-run average interpretation, the expected value of a random variable can also be interpreted as the weighted average of the different possible values of the random variable, with the probabilities (likelihoods) of the respective events being the weights. To justify this statement, we weight (multiply) each of the values $\underline{v}_i$ ($\underline{i} = 1,2,\ldots,\underline{n}$) by its probability, add these $\underline{n}$ products, and divide this sum by the sum of the weights to obtain a weighted average:

$$\frac{v_1\,\underline{P}(\underline{v}_1) + v_2\,\underline{P}(\underline{v}_2) + \ldots + v_n\,\underline{P}(\underline{v}_n)}{\underline{P}(\underline{v}_1) + \underline{P}(\underline{v}_2) + \ldots + \underline{P}(\underline{v}_n)}$$

We know (from the discussion at the end of Section 3.32) that the denominator in the preceding expression equals 1, so that this expression is really identical to Eq. 3.1.

Finally, just as the arithmetic mean for any series of numbers does not have to equal a particular number in the series, the expected value of a random variable does not have to equal a particular value of the random variable. For example, in the calculation of $\underline{E}(\underline{A})$ at the very end of the preceding section, $\underline{E}(\underline{A}) = 9.3$ does not equal any of the possible values of $\underline{A}$ (from Table 3.7).

In the next section of this chapter, we shall show how the concept of the expected value of a random variable can provide a criterion for the solution of a decision problem under uncertainty that was formulated in the first chapter.

3.43   Stock Level Determination Problem.

In Section 1.22 (which the reader should now review) we described a firm which sells a perishable product. The daily demand for this product is either 0,1,2, or 3 units. Each unit stocked at the beginning of the day costs \$2 and sells for \$5, with no salvage value for units left unsold at the end of the day. The firm must decide how many units to stock at the beginning of each day. Since the number of units demanded never exceeds 3, obviously the firm will not consider stocking more than 3 units. An experiment consists of examining the sales record at the end of the day, the set of possible outcomes containing the numbers 0, 1, 2, and 3. The number of units demanded during the day (the outcome of the experiment) together with the number of units stocked at the beginning of the day, will determine the firm's total profit for the day. As Table 1.1 shows, 16 possible total profits could result, depending on the number of units demanded and stocked that day. In Chapter 1, we called these 16 profit figures "decision values". We shall now formulate this problem in terms of concepts so far developed in this chapter, and then use these concepts to solve the problem.

Let $\underline{x}$ denote the possible outcomes of the experiment (i.e., $\underline{x} = 0,1,2,3$). Let $\underline{R}^\circ$ denote the random variable "profit from stocking 0 units" whose value [denoted by $\underline{R}^\circ(\underline{x})$] for any outcome is the total profit associated with that outcome and a be-ginning stock of 0 units. Let $\underline{R}^1$ denote the random variable "profit from stocking 1 unit" whose value [denoted by $\underline{R}^1(\underline{x})$] for any outcome is the total profit associated with that outcome and a beginning stock of 1 unit. Let $\underline{R}^2$ and $\underline{R}^3$ [and $\underline{R}^2(\underline{x})$ and $\underline{R}^3(\underline{x})$] be similarly defined. The values of these random vari-ables, which correspond exactly to the "decision values" listed in the second through fourth columns, respectively, of Table 1.1, are given in Table 3.8. Let the different values of the random variable $\underline{R}^i$ ($\underline{i}$ = 0,1,2,3) be denoted by the (ordi-nary) variable $\underline{r}^i$. From Table 3.8, we see that $\underline{r}^0$ = 0; $\underline{r}^1$ = -2,3; that $\underline{r}^2$ = -4,1,6; and that $\underline{r}^3$ = -6,-1,4,9.

TABLE 3.8

RANDOM VARIABLES R^0, R^1, R^2, AND R^3 DEFINED IN STOCK LEVEL PROBLEM

Outcome of Experiment $\underline{x}$	Value of Random Variable			
	$\underline{R}^0(\underline{x})$	$\underline{R}^1(\underline{x})$	$\underline{R}^2(\underline{x})$	$\underline{R}^3(\underline{x})$
0	0	-2	-4	-6
1	0	3	1	-1
2	0	3	6	4
3	0	3	6	9

Next, assume that the firm is able to assign empirical (or subjective) probabilities to the four simple events possible in this experiment. Specifically, if $\underline{D}$ = $\underline{i}$ ($\underline{i}$ = 0,1,2,3) denotes the event "daily demand is $\underline{i}$ units" and if $\underline{P}(\underline{D}$ = $\underline{i})$ denotes the prob-ability of $\underline{D}$ = $\underline{i}$, then assume that $\underline{P}(\underline{D}$ = 0) = .1, $\underline{P}(\underline{D}$ = 1) = .2, $\underline{P}(\underline{D}$ =2) = .4, and $\underline{P}(\underline{D}$ = 3) = .3. With this information, we can construct the probability distribution for the random variables shown in Table 3.8.

These distributions are shown in Table 3.9, where we em-ploy $\underline{P}(\underline{r}^i)$ to denote the probability of $\underline{r}^i$. We shall use $\underline{R}^2$ to illustrate how these probability distributions are constructed.

$\underline{R}^2$ has three different possible values, viz., $\underline{r}_1^2$ = -4, $\underline{r}_2^2$ = 1, and $\underline{r}_3^2$ = 6. From Table 3.8, we know that $\underline{r}_1^2$ = -4 occurs if the outcome of the experiment is "0 units are demanded". But this outcome corresponds to the simple event $\underline{D}$ = 0 whose probability we know is $\underline{P}(\underline{D} = 0)$ = .1 . Hence, the probability of the value $\underline{r}_1^2$ = -4 occurring is .1. By the same argument, the probability of $\underline{r}_2^2$ = 1 occurring is $\underline{P}(\underline{r}_2^2)$ = .2 . Again from Table 3.8, we know that $\underline{r}_3^2$ = 6 occurs if the outcome of the experiment is either 2 or 3. But these outcomes correspond to the multiple event "2 or 3 units are demanded" whose probability is equal to the sum of the probabilities of the simple events it includes, viz., $\underline{P}(\underline{D}=2)+ \underline{P}(\underline{D}=3)$ = .4 + .3 = .7 . Hence, the probability of the value $\underline{r}_3^2$ = 6 occurring is $\underline{P}(\underline{r}_3^2)$ = .7 . The probabilities for the other random variables are calculated similarly.

TABLE 3.9

PROBABILITY DISTRIBUTIONS FOR RANDOM VARIABLES $\underline{R}^0$, $\underline{R}^1$, $\underline{R}^2$, AND $\underline{R}^3$ DEFINED IN STOCK LEVEL PROBLEM

$\underline{R}^0$		$\underline{R}^1$		$\underline{R}^2$		$\underline{R}^3$	
$\underline{r}^0$	$\underline{P}(\underline{r}^0)$	$\underline{r}^1$	$\underline{P}(\underline{r}^1)$	$\underline{r}^2$	$\underline{P}(\underline{r}^2)$	$\underline{r}^3$	$\underline{P}(\underline{r}^3)$
0	1.0	-2	.1	-4	.1	-6	.1
		3	.9	1	.2	-1	.2
				6	.7	4	.4
						9	.3

We can now use Equation 3.1 to calculate the expected values of the random variables $\underline{R}^0$, $\underline{R}^1$, $\underline{R}^2$, and $\underline{R}^3$:

$\underline{E}(\underline{R}^0)$ = $\underline{r}_1^0\underline{P}(\underline{r}_1^0)$ = 0 × 1.0 = 0

$\underline{E}(\underline{R}^1)$ = $\underline{r}_1^1\underline{P}(\underline{r}_1^1)$ + $\underline{r}_2^1\underline{P}(\underline{r}_2^1)$ = -2 × .1 + 3 × .9 = 2.5

$\underline{E}(\underline{R}^2)$ = $\underline{r}_1^2\underline{P}(\underline{r}_1^2)$ + $\underline{r}_2^2\underline{P}(\underline{r}_2^2)$ + $\underline{r}_3^2\underline{P}(\underline{r}_3^2)$

$\quad$ = -4 × .1 + 1 × .2 + 6 × .7 = 4.0

$\underline{E}(\underline{R}^3)$ = $\underline{r}_1^3\underline{P}(\underline{r}_1^3)$ + $\underline{r}_2^3\underline{P}(\underline{r}_2^3)$ + $\underline{r}_3^3\underline{P}(\underline{r}_3^3)$ + $\underline{r}_4^3\underline{P}(\underline{r}_4^3)$

$\quad$ = -6(.1) + (-1)(.2) + 4(.4) + 9(.3) = 3.5

We see that the random variable $\underline{R}^2$ yields a maximum expected value of $\underline{E}(\underline{R}^2)$ = 4.0 .

But $\underline{R}^2$ corresponds to the decision to stock (to the act or policy of stocking) 2 units daily. Thus, from the definition of expected value, if we stock 2 units each day for many days, we expect

to earn a profit of $4 per day on the average in the long run.
This long-run average profit derived from a decision to stock
2 units each day is greater than the long-run average profit
that might be derived from any other decision (i.e., any other
stock level). Hence, if we adopt maximum expected value as
a criterion, the best decision is to stock 2 units daily. The decision problem under uncertainty posed in Chapter 1 has been
solved.

3.44   Maximum Expected Value as a Criterion for "Best" Decisions.

How valid a criterion for identifying the best decision is maximum expected profit? In very many cases it is perfectly
valid, since in very many decision situations the objective of
the firm is the maximization of the long-run average profit[1]
from a given decision that must be frequently repeated, i.e.,
the same decision situation occurs again and again. Even if
the decision has to be made, and the profit earned, just once
(and not every day as in our illustration), the maximum expected value criterion is valid since it represents the maximization of the weighted average (with probability of occurrence being the weight) of the profits that could result from
different decisions.

 While maximum expected value is an extremely useful criterion for decision-making under uncertainty, this is not to say that it
is always applicable. For example, in the illustration of this section, if the firm wanted to follow a policy of never sending a customer home empty-handed, it would have to stock 3 units daily
even though $\underline{E}(\underline{R}^3) = 3.5 < \underline{E}(\underline{R}^2) = 4.0$. Again, if the firm wanted
to follow a policy of never incurring a loss on this product greater
than $3 (i.e., a profit smaller than $-3), it would have to stock 1
unit daily, since the smallest possible profit when 1 unit is stocked
daily is $-2, while a profit as low as $-4 could be earned when
2 units are stocked daily. This sort of discussion, which leads
into the theory of utility, is beyond the scope of this book and we
shall leave it right here. In the remainder of this text, we shall
assume that maximum expected profit (or minimum expected cost)
is a valid decision criterion.

---

[1] Expected value can also be used as a criterion for the best decision in problems involving the minimization of cost. Section 3.45 will present such a case.

TABLE 3.10

DEFECTIVE RATES AND PROBABILITIES
FOR MACHINES A, B, AND C

Defective Rate	Probability of Stated Defective Rate for Machine		
	A	B	C
.01	.5	.6	.7
.02	.5	.3	.1
.03	—	.1	.1
.04	—	—	.1
	1.0	1.0	1.0

3.45   Equipment Selection Problem.   A manufacturer receives an order to produce 1,000 units of a particular product. Three machines, A, B, and C, are currently available, and this product can be produced on any one of them. From past experience with similar orders, the manufacturer knows that a certain percentage of the output of these machines will be defective, the particular defective rate [2] observed depending on the quality of the machine set-up. Moreover, defective units are produced in a random pattern. The possible defective rates for these machines, together with their empirical probabilities of occurrence, are given in Table 3.10. Each defective unit produced can be made acceptable by reworking at a cost of $2.00 per unit. Which machine should the manufacturer select to produce this order, assuming that his only concern is to keep down reworking costs?

We can consider this problem in terms of an empirical experiment. This experiment is the setting-up of a machine. The outcomes of this experiment are the possible defective rates that could occur. If we let $\underline{x}^A$ denote the possible outcomes from the experiment of setting up Machine A, we have (from Table 3.10), $\underline{x}^A$ = .01, .02. Similar notation (and use of Table 3.10) yields $\underline{x}^B$ = .01, .02, .03 and $\underline{x}^C$ = .01, .02, .03, .04 as the possible outcomes from the experiments of setting up Machines B and C, respectively. Note that we have described three different experiments.

---

[2] A defective rate of, e.g., .01 means that 1 percent of the output produced will be defective.

Let $\underline{v}^{\underline{A}}$ denote the random variable "rework cost when Machine $\underline{A}$ is used". Then the different possible values [denoted by $\underline{v}^{\underline{A}}(\underline{x}^{\underline{A}})$] of $\underline{v}^{\underline{A}}$ are $\underline{v}^{\underline{A}}(.01) = 20$ and $\underline{v}^{\underline{A}}(.02) = 40$. These values are determined from the formula

rework cost for Machine $\underline{A}$ = size of order $\times \underline{x}^{\underline{A}} \times$ unit rework

cost

$= 1{,}000 \times .01 \times \$2 = \$20$ for $\underline{x}^{\underline{A}} = .01$

$= 1{,}000 \times .02 \times \$2 = \$40$ for $\underline{x}^{\underline{A}} = .02$

Adopting similar notation for the other two experiments (i.e., the set-ups of Machines $\underline{B}$ and $\underline{C}$), the reader can verify the results shown in Table 3.11.

TABLE 3.11

RANDOM VARIABLES $\underline{v}^{\underline{A}}$, $\underline{v}^{\underline{B}}$, AND $\underline{v}^{\underline{C}}$

$\underline{v}^{\underline{A}}$		$\underline{v}^{\underline{B}}$		$\underline{v}^{\underline{C}}$	
$\underline{x}^{\underline{A}}$	$\underline{v}^{\underline{A}}(\underline{x}^{\underline{A}})$	$\underline{x}^{\underline{B}}$	$\underline{v}^{\underline{B}}(\underline{x}^{\underline{B}})$	$\underline{x}^{\underline{C}}$	$\underline{v}^{\underline{C}}(\underline{x}^{\underline{C}})$
.01	20	.01	20	.01	20
.02	40	.02	40	.02	40
—	—	.03	60	.03	60
—	—	—	—	.04	80

Each possible value of the random variables shown in Table 3.11 is associated with one of the simple events possible in the relevant experiment. The probabilities of these simple events, and thus of the values of the random variables, are given by the basic data of Table 3.10. If we use $\underline{v}^{\underline{A}}$ to denote the different values of $\underline{v}^{\underline{A}}$ (and $\underline{v}^{\underline{B}}$ and $\underline{v}^{\underline{C}}$ for $\underline{v}^{\underline{B}}$ and $\underline{v}^{\underline{C}}$), and $P(\underline{v}^{\underline{A}})$ to denote the probability of $\underline{v}^{\underline{A}}$ [and $\underline{P}(\underline{v}^{\underline{B}})$ and $\underline{P}(\underline{v}^{\underline{C}})$ the probability of $v^{\underline{B}}$ and $v^{\underline{C}}$], we can use Eq. 3.1 to determine the expected values of the three random variables:

$$\underline{E}(\underline{v}^{\underline{A}}) = \underline{v}^{\underline{A}}_{\overline{1}}\underline{P}(\underline{v}^{\underline{A}}_{\overline{1}}) + \underline{v}^{\underline{A}}_{\overline{2}}\underline{P}(\underline{v}^{\underline{A}}_{\overline{2}}) = 20(.5) + 40(.5) = 30$$

$$\underline{E}(\underline{V}^{\underline{B}}) = \underline{v}_{\overline{1}}^{\underline{B}}\underline{P}(\underline{v}_{\overline{1}}^{\underline{B}}) + \underline{v}_{\overline{2}}^{\underline{B}}\underline{P}(\underline{v}_{\overline{2}}^{\underline{B}}) + \underline{v}_{\overline{3}}^{\underline{B}}\underline{P}(\underline{v}_{\overline{3}}^{\underline{B}}) = 20(.6) + 40(.3) +$$
$$60(.1) = 30$$
$$\underline{E}(\underline{V}^{\underline{C}}) = \underline{v}_{\overline{1}}^{\underline{C}}\underline{P}(\underline{v}_{\overline{1}}^{\underline{C}}) + \underline{v}_{\overline{2}}^{\underline{C}}\underline{P}(\underline{v}_{\overline{2}}^{\underline{C}}) + \underline{v}_{\overline{3}}^{\underline{C}}\underline{P}(\underline{v}_{\overline{3}}^{\underline{C}}) + \underline{v}_{\overline{4}}^{\underline{C}}\underline{P}(\underline{v}_{\overline{4}}^{\underline{C}})$$
$$= 20(.7) + 40(.1) + 60(.1) + 80(.1) = 32$$

Since $\underline{E}(\underline{V}^{\underline{A}}) = \underline{E}(\underline{V}^{\underline{B}}) < \underline{E}(\underline{V}^{\underline{C}})$, we know that the expected cost of reworking will be less with Machines $\underline{A}$ and $\underline{B}$ than with $\underline{C}$. The best decision, using minimum expected cost as the criterion, would be to select either Machine $\underline{A}$ or $\underline{B}$ for this job.

Notice that in the problem discussed in this section, the "best" decision involved a comparison of the expected values of three random variables, each of which was defined for a different experiment. In the problem discussed in Section 3.43, the "best" decision involved a comparison of four random variables, each of which was defined for the same experiment.

3.5   PERSPECTIVE

In the preceding chapter, we described and illustrated three types of stochastic experiments, formulated probability definitions for each type, and examined the implications of these definitions. In this chapter we defined and illustrated the important and related concepts of random variable, probability distribution, and expected value. In the next chapter we shall apply these results directly to specific business decision problems. Chapter 5 will use these same results to develop additional concepts from the theory of probability. These later concepts will then be applied to business decision problems in Chapters 6 and 7.

3.6   DISCUSSION AND REVIEW QUESTIONS

1. How are the concepts random variable, probability distribution, and expected value related?

2. Give an example, other than the one used in the text, of an identity random variable.

3. Give two interpretations of the expected value of a random variable.

4. Is maximum (or minimum) expected value a valid criterion for identifying the "best decision"?

3.7   EXERCISES

1. A box contains 1 red, 3 black, and 6 white golf balls. An
experiment consists of shaking the box, and then reaching in and
selecting 1 golf ball. A random variable $\underline{V}$ is defined for this set
of possible outcomes. Let $\underline{x}$ denote the outcome of the experiment
($\underline{x}$ = $\underline{R}$, $\underline{B}$, or $\underline{W}$, where the letters signify, respectively, red,
black, or white ball). The value of $\underline{V}$, denoted by $\underline{V}(\underline{x})$, is 5 if
$\underline{x}$ = $\underline{R}$, 10 if $\underline{x}$ = $\underline{B}$, and 12 if $\underline{x}$ = $\underline{W}$.

  (a) Construct a table, similar to Tables 3.1 to 3.4,
      which shows $\underline{V}$.
  (b) Construct a table which shows the probability
      distribution of $\underline{V}$.
  (c) Calculate the expected value of $\underline{V}$. (Ans.: 10.7)

2. A box contains 1 red, 2 black, 3 orange, 4 yellow, 5 white,
and 5 green golf balls. An experiment consists of shaking the box,
and then reaching in and selecting 1 golf ball. Let the value of the
random variable $\underline{Z}$ be 10 if $\underline{x}$ = $\underline{R}$ or $\underline{B}$, 12 if $\underline{x}$ = $\underline{O}$, $\underline{Y}$ or $\underline{W}$, and 18
if $\underline{x}$ = $\underline{G}$.

  (a) Construct a table showing $\underline{Z}$.
  (b) Construct a table showing the probability distribu-
      tion of $\underline{Z}$.
  (c) Calculate the expected value of $\underline{Z}$.

3. A pair of coins is tossed and the head-tail pattern on the
two upturned faces observed. Let the value of the random variable
$\underline{V}$ be 3 times the number of heads observed. For this experiment
prepare a diagram, similar to that shown in Fig. 3.1, which sup-
ports the argument, given at the end of Section 3.32, that the sum
of the probabilities in a probability distribution must be 1.

4. It is known that either one percent, two percent, three
percent, four percent, or five percent of the parts turned out by
Machine $\underline{A}$ are defective. The particular defective rate observed
depends on the quality of the machine set-up. The empirical

probabilities of these defective rates are, respectively, .3, .2, .2, .2, and .1.

(a) Describe the experiment generating these outcomes.
(b) If Machine A now produces an order for 5,000 parts, and if the cost of reworking each defective part is $.50, what is the expected rework cost?   (Ans.: $65.00)
(c) This order can alternatively be produced by Machines B, C, or D. Table 3.12 shows the defective rates of these machines, together with their probabilities. Which machine should the firm use to produce this order? In answering this question, formulate the problem in terms of random variables and probability distributions.

TABLE 3.12

DEFECTIVE RATES FOR MACHINES B, C, D

Defective Rate x	$P(x)$		
	B	C	D
.01		.1	.4
.02	.4	.2	.2
.03	.5	.7	.1
.04	.1	—	.1
.05	—	—	.1
.06	—	—	.1

5. A firm is considering two investment opportunities, each requiring the same capital outlay and having the same life. The first possible investment, a bond purchase, is certain to yield an annual return of five percent. The second possible investment, a land purchase, will result in an annual return of either twenty percent or two percent; the higher rate will be realized if the government decides to construct a major highway through the property. Assume that the risks involved in either investment are identical. If the firm is to be completely indifferent between the two investments, what must the probability of the event "the government decides to construct a major highway through the property" be? [Hint: set $.2x + .02(1-x) = .05$.]

6. A firm is considering two investment opportunities, each requiring the same capital outlay, and having the same life and risk. The first investment, a new novelty consumer item, will return thirty percent if the economy does not have a downturn, but only one percent if a recession does occur. The second investment, government bonds, will yield a certain return of four percent. If the firm is to be indifferent between the two investments, what must be the probability of the event "a recession occurs"?

4 ▶ EXPECTED VALUE AND MONTE CARLO MODELS FOR INVENTORY CONTROL

4.1 MOTIVATION

This chapter is concerned with applying the concepts introduced in the preceding chapters to two models for inventory control. The first model is an expected value model similar to the one discussed in Section 3.43. The problem analyzed here, however, exhibits a more realistic demand schedule, explicitly treats the possibility of salvage value, and introduces the notion of the value of perfect information. After treating this model, we shall present a Monte Carlo simulation model for a different type of inventory control problem.

4.2 INVENTORY CONTROL FOR A PERISHABLE PRODUCT WITH SALVAGE VALUE

The manager of a supermarket has fresh loaves of bread delivered at the beginning of each day. He wishes to determine the optimum standing order, i.e., the optimum number of

loaves that should be delivered daily, for the coming year.
The number of loaves demanded daily fluctuates, but, on the
basis of considerable experience and analysis, the manager
feels that these fluctuations are not appreciably affected by
seasonal factors (climate and custom), cyclical factors (pros-
perity and recession), and trend factors (long-term growth re-
flecting population and standard of living changes). Moreover,
during the past year there were no irregular factors, e.g., a
labor strike which closed the supermarket, that could have
caused the fluctuations shown in the historical record of the
quantity demanded daily.

Hence, the manager feels confident that stochastic factors alone are essentially responsible for these fluctuations
in the number of loaves demanded daily. Furthermore, he
believes that the stochastic factors influencing next year's
demand will be the same as those operating this year.

4.21 Demand Probabilities. Given these conditions, the
manager can view the examination of the sales record at the
end of any given day next year as the performance of a stochastic experiment, the outcome of which will be the number
of units demanded that day. Since sales records for the past
year are available, the manager is able to calculate the empirical probabilities of the events relevant to this experiment.

Table 4.1 shows the quantity demanded for the past 350
days, summarized in intervals of 100 loaves. We see that the
number of loaves demanded daily fluctuates between 300 and
999. Within each of the seven intervals shown, we would expect that on the average the number of loaves demanded would
approximately equal the midpoint of the interval. For example, some of the 40 daily demands which fell in the interval
"400 but under 500" would be equal to the midpoint value 450,
some would be under it, and others over it; but these 40 demands should, nonetheless, average about 450. Since the midpoints are, in this way, representative of the intervals, we
shall restrict our choice of possible standing orders to these
seven values. This will greatly simplify the required calculations, and will yield a solution that will not be significantly
different from what would be obtained if we considered all in-
tegers from 300 to 999 as possible standing orders.

TABLE 4.1

DAILY DEMAND FOR BREAD, PAST YEAR

(1) Number of Loaves of Bread Demanded Daily	(2) Midpoint of Interval ($\underline{i}$)	(3) Number of Days in Which Stated Number of Loaves Were Demanded	(4) Simple Event "Daily Demand is $\underline{i}$ Units" ($\underline{D} = \underline{i}$)	(5) Probability of Event $\underline{D} = \underline{i}$ $[\underline{P}(\underline{D} = \underline{i})]$
300 but under 400	350	20	$\underline{D} = 350$	.057
400 but under 500	450	40	$\underline{D} = 450$	.114
500 but under 600	550	80	$\underline{D} = 550$	.228
600 but under 700	650	100	$\underline{D} = 650$	.286
700 but under 800	750	70	$\underline{D} = 750$	.200
800 but under 900	850	30	$\underline{D} = 850$	.086
900 but under 1000	950	10	$\underline{D} = 950$	.029
		350		1.000

In Table 4.1, the seven midpoints (denoted by i) are recorded in column 2. These midpoints make up a list of seven
collectively exhaustive and mutually exclusive outcomes for
this experiment. The seven corresponding simple events
(denoted by $D = i$) are shown in column 4, and their probabilities [denoted by $P(D = i)$] in column 5. These probabilities
are determined, using Definition 2.2, by dividing each of the
entries in column 3 by 350.

4.22 **Cost and Revenue Data.** While the manager now has
some idea how the daily demand for bread is likely to vary
over the next year, he cannot rationally decide on the optimum
standing order until certain cost and revenue data are considered. He knows that the cost of each loaf of bread is $.25
and its selling price is $.30. Furthermore, loaves left unsold
by the end of the day can be resold to an animal food processor for $.10; that is, day-old bread has a salvage value of
$.10.

4.23 **Random Variables.** Let x denote the outcome of the
experiment performed by examining the sales record at the
end of the day; then $x = 350, 450, \ldots, 950$. Next, let R^{350} denote
the random variable "profit from a standing order of 350
units" whose value [denoted by $R^{350}(x)$] for any outcome x
is the total profit associated with that outcome and a standing
order of 350 units; in general, let R^i ($i = 350, 450, \ldots, 950$) denote the random variable "profit from a standing order of i
units" whose value [denoted by $R^i(x)$] for any outcome x is
the total profit associated with that outcome and a standing
order of i units. We need to determine the values of these
random variables.

These values can be determined from the following equations:

$$R^i(x) = px + s(i - x) - ci, \qquad x < i \qquad (4.1)$$

$$R^i(x) = (p - c)i \qquad\qquad x \geq i \qquad (4.2)$$

where

$\underline{x}$ denotes the outcome of the experiment, i.e., the number of units demanded

$\underline{i}$ denotes the standing order
$\underline{p}$ denotes the price of a loaf of bread
$\underline{c}$ denotes the cost of a loaf of bread
$\underline{s}$ denotes the salvage value of a loaf of bread

(in the problem presently under discussion, $\underline{p}$ = .30, $\underline{c}$ = .25, and $\underline{s}$ = .10). Eq. 4.1 is applicable whenever the number of loaves demanded for the day is less than the standing order. The first term represents the revenue earned from units demanded and sold during the day to supermarket customers; the second term represents the revenue earned at the end of the day from selling left-over units, i.e., units stocked but not demanded by supermarket customers, to the food processor; the third term represents the cost of the bread ordered from and delivered by the supplying bakery at the beginning of the day. Eq. 4.2 is applicable when the number of loaves demanded during the day equals or exceeds the number ordered; it represents profit per unit ($\underline{p}$ - $\underline{c}$) times the number of units sold.

To illustrate, if $\underline{x}$ = 550 and $\underline{i}$ = 350, since $\underline{x}$ > $\underline{i}$, Eq. 4.2 is applicable and $\underline{R}^{350}(550)$ = (.30 - .25) 350 = 17.50. If $\underline{x}$ = 450 and $\underline{i}$ = 850, since $\underline{x}$ < $\underline{i}$, Eq. (4.1) is applicable and $\underline{R}^{850}(450)$ = .30(450) + .10(850 - 450) - .25(850) = -37.50. Table 4.2 shows the values of the seven random variables $\underline{R}^{i}$ calculated from Eqs. 4.1 and 4.2 .

4.24 **Probability Distributions.**   Let $\underline{r}^{i}$ denote the different possible values of $\underline{R}^{i}$ ($\underline{i}$ = 350,450,...,950), and let $\underline{P}(\underline{r}^{i})$ denote the probability of $\underline{r}^{i}$. Table 4.3 shows $\underline{r}^{i}$ and $\underline{P}(\underline{r}^{i})$ for $\underline{i}$ = 350,450,...,950; that is, it shows the probability distributions for the random variables $\underline{R}^{350}, \underline{R}^{450}, ..., \underline{R}^{950}$. The $\underline{r}^{i}$ are obtained from Table 4.2. The $\underline{P}(\underline{r}^{i})$ are determined from the information given in Tables 4.1 and 4.2.

TABLE 4.2

RANDOM VARIABLES $\underline{R}^{350}, \underline{R}^{450}, ..., \underline{R}^{950}$

Outcome of Experiment $\underline{x}$	Value of Random Variable						
	$\underline{R}^{350}(\underline{x})$	$\underline{R}^{450}(\underline{x})$	$\underline{R}^{550}(\underline{x})$	$\underline{R}^{650}(\underline{x})$	$\underline{R}^{750}(\underline{x})$	$\underline{R}^{850}(\underline{x})$	$R^{950}(\underline{x})$
350	17.50	2.50	-12.50	-27.50	-42.50	-57.50	-72.50
450	17.50	22.50	7.50	-7.50	-22.50	-37.50	-52.50
550	17.50	22.50	27.50	12.50	-2.50	-17.50	-32.50
650	17.50	22.50	27.50	32.50	17.50	2.50	-12.50
750	17.50	22.50	27.50	32.50	37.50	22.50	7.50
850	17.50	22.50	27.50	32.50	37.50	42.50	27.50
950	17.50	22.50	27.50	32.50	37.50	42.50	47.50

TABLE 4.3

PROBABILITY DISTRIBUTIONS FOR THE RANDOM VARIABLES $\underline{R}^{350}, \underline{R}^{450}, ..., \underline{R}^{950}$

R^{350}		R^{450}		R^{550}		R^{650}		R^{750}		R^{850}		R^{950}	
$\underline{r}^{350}$	$\underline{P}(\underline{r}^{350})$	$\underline{r}^{450}$	$\underline{P}(\underline{r}^{450})$	$\underline{r}^{550}$	$\underline{P}(\underline{r}^{550})$	$\underline{r}^{650}$	$\underline{P}(\underline{r}^{650})$	$\underline{r}^{750}$	$\underline{P}(\underline{r}^{750})$	$\underline{r}^{850}$	$\underline{P}(\underline{r}^{850})$	$\underline{r}^{950}$	$\underline{P}(\underline{r}^{950})$
17.50	1.000	2.50	.057	-12.50	.057	-27.50	.057	-42.50	.057	-57.50	.057	-72.50	.057
		22.50	.943	7.50	.114	-7.50	.114	-22.50	.114	-37.50	.114	-52.50	.114
				27.50	.829	12.50	.228	-2.50	.228	-17.50	.228	-32.50	.228
						32.50	.601	17.50	.286	2.50	.286	-12.50	.286
								37.50	.315	22.50	.200	7.50	.200
										42.50	.115	27.50	.086
												47.50	.029
	1.000		1.000		1.000		1.000		1.000		1.000		1.000

For example, for $\underline{R}^{650}$ Table 4.2 shows that four different values are possible: i.e., $\underline{r}^{650}$ = -27.50, -7.50, 12.50, and 32.50. $\underline{r}_1^{650}$ = -27.50 is observed if the outcome x_1 = 350 occurs; but this outcome corresponds to the simple event "daily demand is 350 units" (i.e., to $\underline{D}$ = 350), whose probability, from Table 4.1, is $\underline{P}(\underline{D}$ = 350) = .057. Hence, $\underline{P}(\underline{r}_1^{650})$ = .057. Similarly, since the values $\underline{r}_2^{650}$ = -7.50 and $\underline{r}_3^{650}$ = 12.50 are observed if the simple events $\underline{D}$ = 450 and $\underline{D}$ = 550 occur, respectively, we have $\underline{P}(\underline{r}_2^{650})$ = $\underline{P}(\underline{D}$ = 450) = .114 and $\underline{P}(\underline{r}_3^{650})$ = $\underline{P}(\underline{D}$ = 550) = .228. The value $\underline{r}_4^{650}$ = 32.50 is observed (in Table 4.2) if the multiple event "$\underline{D}$ = 650 or $\underline{D}$ = 750 or $\underline{D}$ = 850 or $\underline{D}$ = 950" occurs, and the probability of this multiple event is the sum of the probabilities of the simple events it includes, viz., $\underline{P}(\underline{D}$ = 650)+ $\underline{P}(\underline{D}$ = 750) + $\underline{P}(\underline{D}$ = 850) + $\underline{P}(\underline{D}$ = 950) = .286 + .200 + .086 + .029 = .601. The other $\underline{P}(\underline{r}^i)$ in Table 4.3 are calculated similarly (the reader should check a few to test his understanding of the procedure).

4.25   Expected Values.

We now use Eq. 3.1 to compute the expected values of the random variables $\underline{R}^{350}$, $\underline{R}^{450}$,..., $\underline{R}^{950}$. For example,

$$\underline{E}(\underline{R}^{350}) = \underline{r}^{350}\underline{P}(\underline{r}_i^{350}) = 17.50(1.00) = 17.50$$

$$\underline{E}(\underline{R}^{450}) = \underline{r}_1^{450}\underline{P}(\underline{r}_1^{450}) + \underline{r}_2^{450}\underline{P}(\underline{r}_2^{450}) = 2.50(.057)$$
$$+ 22.50(.943) = 21.36$$

$$\underline{E}(\underline{R}^{550}) = \underline{r}_1^{550}\underline{P}(\underline{r}_1^{550}) + \underline{r}_2^{550}\underline{P}(\underline{r}_2^{550}) + r_3^{550}\underline{P}(\underline{r}_3^{550})$$
$$= -12.50(.057) + 7.50(.114) + 27.50(.829) = 22.94$$

These and the computations for the expected values of the remaining random variables are summarized in Table 4.4.

We see that the random variable R^{550} yields the greatest expected value [equal to $E(R^{550})$ = 22.94]. This random variable represents the decision to place a standing order for 550 units daily. Thus, if we use maximum expected value as the decision criterion, the best decision for this inventory problem is to select an order quantity of 550 units daily.

TABLE 4.4

EXPECTED VALUES FOR RANDOM
VARIABLES $\underline{R}^{350}$, $\underline{R}^{450}$, ... $\underline{R}^{950}$

i	$\underline{E}(\underline{R}^{\underline{i}})$
350	17.50
450	21.36
550	22.94
650	19.96
750	11.26
850	- 1.44
950	-15.86

4.3   VALUE OF PERFECT INFORMATION

The problem formulated at the beginning of Section 4.2 has been solved. However, it will be instructive to continue our analysis of that problem.

Suppose a consultant now approaches the supermarket manager and points out that the supermarket's expected profit on bread can be increased in the long-run if very close esti-mates of the next day's demand can be obtained. The consult-ant is planning, by use of consumer panel and market survey techniques, to prepare, each day, forecasts of the next day's sales of many kinds of products. For a fee of $10 per day this consultant will include forecasts of the daily demand for bread at this supermarket. Should the manager purchase this infor-mation?

We can answer this question by first answering a more theoretical one. Specifically, if the manager could obtain per-fect forecasts of tomorrow's demand, i.e., if he could obtain perfect information, how much would this be worth? We an-swer this question as follows.

If the manager knew, beforehand, that $\underline{x}$ loaves of bread would be demanded during the next day, he would place an order for exactly $\underline{x}$ loaves to be received at the beginning of the next

day. At the end of the next day, he will have no loaves of bread
left over, and every loaf that was demanded, i.e., that could
have been sold, will have been available and sold. It would be
impossible for the manager to increase his profit for the day,
i.e., no other order would have resulted in more profit.

Now from Table 4.1 we know that the possible daily demands are 350, 450, . . . , and 950. Each day one of these
numbers is demanded, and, with perfect information, each day
the supermarket will have exactly that number on hand and will
earn the maximum possible profit for that daily demand. This
maximum profit is .30-.25 = .05 cents per loaf times the number of loaves demanded. Since each daily demand is an outcome
of a stochastic experiment and since each such outcome generates a number (viz., the profit possible with perfect information), we have just described a random variable. To be more
specific, let $\underline{R}^{I}$ denote the random variable "profit with perfect information" whose value for any outcome $\underline{x}$ is the total
daily profit associated with that outcome when perfect information is available. Columns 1 and 2 of Table 4.5 show $\underline{R}^{I}$.

TABLE 4.5

PROBABILITY DISTRIBUTION FOR RANDOM VARIABLE $\underline{R}^{I}$
(PROFIT WITH PERFECT INFORMATION)

(1) $\underline{x}$	(2) $\underline{R}^{I}(x) = \underline{r}^{I} =$ $(.30-.25)\underline{x}$	(3) $P(\underline{r}^{I})$	(4) $E(\underline{R}^{I})$ (2) × (3)
350	17.50	.057	.9975
450	22.50	.114	2.5650
550	27.50	.228	6.2700
650	32.50	.286	9.2950
750	37.50	.200	7.5000
850	42.50	.086	3.6550
950	47.50	.029	1.3775
			31.6600

The <u>different</u> possible values $\underline{r}^I$ of $\underline{R}^I$ correspond exactly to $\underline{R}^I(\underline{x})$. Moreover, $\underline{P}(\underline{r}_1^I) = \underline{P}(17.50) = \underline{P}(\underline{D} = 350)$, $\underline{P}(\underline{r}_2^I) = \underline{P}(22.50) = \underline{P}(\underline{D} = 450), \ldots, \underline{P}(\underline{r}_7^I) = \underline{P}(47.50) = \underline{P}(\underline{D} = 950)$. This probability distribution for $\underline{R}^I$ is shown in columns 2 and 3 of Table 4.5.

Column 4, obtained by multiplying columns 2 and 3, shows that $\underline{E}(\underline{R}^I) = 31.66$. That is, the expected value of daily profit, when perfect information is available, is $31.66.

From the preceding section, we know that the greatest possible expected profit under uncertainty, i.e., without perfect information, is $\underline{E}(\underline{R}^{550}) = 22.94$. Naturally, $\underline{E}(\underline{R}^I) > \underline{E}(\underline{R}^{550})$. However, it is only $\underline{E}(\underline{R}^I) - \underline{E}(\underline{R}^{550}) = 31.66 - 22.94 = 8.72$ greater. This means it would not be profitable to pay more than $8.72 daily for perfect information. For example, if we paid $9.00 > $8.72 for perfect information, our expected daily profit would be $\underline{E}(\underline{R}^I)$ minus the cost of this information or $31.66 - $9.00 = $22.66. But this is less than the expected profit of the best decision under uncertainty, $\underline{E}(\underline{R}^{550}) = $22.94.

Hence, we conclude that even if perfect information is available, it is never worth more than the difference between the expected profit with perfect information and the expected profit of the best decision (maximum expected value) under uncertainty. This means that less than perfect information, which is what we will typically get in practice, must be worth even less than this difference.

To return to our original question, since the consultant is charging $10.00 > $8.72 per day for his additional (and necessarily less than perfect) information on the daily demand for bread, it would not be profitable to purchase his forecast.

The concept of the value of perfect information is vital in the analysis of the value of additional information obtained through sampling and further investigation. However, to go further at this point would take us into the field of what is known as statistical decision theory. While we introduce some additional concepts from this field in the next chapter, to attempt more now would be beyond the scope of this text.

4.4   MONTE CARLO SIMULATION MODEL FOR INVENTORY CONTROL

In Section 4.2, the inventory control problem examined required the determination only of the optimum order quantity for a perishable product with salvage value and stochastic demand. The objective of the firm was the maximization of expected profit.

In this section, we treat an inventory problem which requires the determination of both the optimum order quantity and optimum order level for a nonperishable product with both stochastic demand and lead time. Moreover, the objective of the firm is the minimization of expected total inventory costs (i.e., holding, order, and shortage costs).

These differences in the two models will become clearer as we proceed. First, however, we must examine the technique of Monte Carlo simulation.

4.41   Monte Carlo Models in General.

Monte Carlo models can be applied when the problem under analysis involves variables whose values are determined by stochastic experiments, i.e., when the problem contains one or more random variables, and when sufficient data or experience is available for the construction of probability distributions for these variables. The Monte Carlo method is a trial and error procedure. However, this procedure takes place in an artificial (or simulated) environment which closely resembles (simulates) the real world situation (hence, the origin of the term "simulation" used to describe the method).

To illustrate, a model is constructed which captures the basic attributes of the real world situation. Then an arbitrary decision is fed into this model. The Monte Carlo technique generates the results that would be associated with this decision over a long period of time (over many experiments). Then another decision is fed into the model, and the results of this decision are compared to those of the first decision. In this way, the results of all possible decisions are generated and compared, and by trial and error the best decision is found.

Since the various possible decisions are not tried in the real world (but in a model), the errors associated with poor decisions do not really hurt the firm, as they would if the trial and error procedure were actually carried out in the real world. Moreover, in the real world, the length of time it would take to obtain a fair assessment of each decision could be so long that the underlying conditions upon which the decisions are based could eventually change. Thus, even after a very long period of time, the firm may not have determined the best decision, since the results of decisions made under different sets of conditions are not comparable. In short, Monte Carlo methods make trial and error solutions possible in situations not otherwise suited to such solutions.

Quite often, Monte Carlo models present the only method for obtaining solutions to complex problems involving many variables and relationships. Moreover, even when an analytical (as opposed to trial and error) solution is possible, Monte Carlo methods can give quicker and more easily obtained results.

The term "Monte Carlo" has been attached to the procedure just described because the technique used to generate results is based on the concept of "random numbers". We turn to this concept in the next section.

4.42   **Random Numbers.**   Assume we have a box which contains ten metal disks which are physically identical. That is, each disk has exactly the same shape, weight, density, and structure. The disks differ from one another only in that each has one of the ten one-digit numbers 1,2,...,8,9,0 painted on its surface; that is to say, the entire set of ten numbers is allocated to the set of ten disks so that every disk has a number painted on it and no number appears on more than one disk.

An experiment, hereafter referred to as the "box experiment", consists of: 1) having the box shaken, so that the disks are thoroughly mixed; 2) having a blindfolded person select one disk from the box; 3) having a second person record the number on this disk; and 4) returning the disk to the box. This is an a priori experiment in which the set of ten collectively exhaustive and mutually exclusive outcomes are the numbers 1,2,...,8,9, and 0. The probabilities of the ten simple events "the number 1 is selected", "the number 2 is selected",..., "the number 9 is selected", "the number 0 is selected" are

each 1/10 = .1.   Since chance alone determines the outcome of
this experiment, the number observed is called a <u>random
number</u>.[1]

If this experiment is performed, say, 10,000 times, a list
of 10,000 one-digit random numbers will be generated. In each
experiment, the probability of any particular number occurring
will always be fixed at .1.   Since the numbers are generated by
chance, and since all numbers are equally likely to occur, this
list will have no discernable pattern. That is, numbers will
appear as if they were "written at random" (which, in fact,
they were), with no one number or series of numbers forming
any predictable relationship.

Assume, now, that the same experiment is performed
10,000 times with 100, instead of 10, disks in the box, each
disk having one of the 100 two-digit numbers 01, 02,...,98,99,
00 painted on it. A list of 10,000 two-digit random numbers
will be produced, the probability of any given number occurring on any given experiment being 1/100 = .01.   In the same
way, if 10,000 experiments are performed with 1,000, instead
of 100, disks in the box, with each disk having one of the 1,000
three-digit numbers 001,002,...,998,999,000 painted on it, a
list of 10,000 three-digit random numbers will be produced;
the probability of any given number occurring on any experiment would be 1/100 = .001.   In this same fashion, a list of
any size containing random numbers of any size can be generated.

In practice, these numbers do not have to be generated by
a person reaching into a box, as just described. Rather, the
same result can be obtained by programming a mathematical
formula into a computer. However, even this short cut is unnecessary, since published tables of random numbers are
readily available.[2]

In what follows, the reader can view Table 4.6 as a table
of two-digit random numbers generated by the author either

---

[1] Strictly speaking, since each random number has the same probability of occurrence,
the set of possible outcomes is called a set of "uniformly distributed random numbers" to distinguish it from a set produced by an experiment in which the outcomes
are not equally likely.

[2] See, for example, The RAND Corporation, "A Million Random Digits", Free Press,
Glencoe, Illinois, 1955.

TABLE 4.6

200 TWO-DIGIT RANDOM NUMBERS

50	17	33	05	94	05	77	02	10	01	66	45	68	28	51	65	68	51	61	85
72	22	21	56	86	01	55	29	51	84	06	57	66	46	52	12	94	36	69	11
56	57	15	70	43	45	73	53	82	87	57	18	57	82	77	09	74	24	45	28
82	82	94	70	19	11	22	68	16	69	47	24	48	87	56	68	20	87	48	95
48	88	66	07	94	76	70	70	15	38	17	06	18	09	78	05	84	16	47	76
09	54	42	01	80	06	06	26	57	79	45	65	06	59	33	70	32	79	24	35
01	50	29	54	46	11	43	09	62	32	88	41	07	52	03	34	53	45	08	88
91	98	48	07	64	93	29	69	44	72	58	51	23	26	00	36	76	83	80	52
24	41	53	83	52	87	20	01	19	36	62	19	19	23	16	34	38	38	07	41
24	94	38	96	18	24	94	73	33	98	70	53	61	89	26	38	34	46	84	28

by means of the box experiment described above or, equivalently, by mathematical formula and the computer. If we think of Table 4.6 as a summary of the results of 200 box experiments, assume that a reading of the columns from top to bottom corresponds to the order in which the 200 box experiments were performed. For example, 50 and 72 are the first two outcomes (first two random numbers obtained, and 17 and 22 (at the top of the second column) are the eleventh and twelfth outcomes obtained.

Although Table 4.6 presents two-digit random numbers, one-digit random numbers can be obtained from this table simply by ignoring the first (or second) digit in each two-digit number. In effect, this would assume that the experiment consists of selecting a disk and ignoring the second digit on each disk. Since 10 out of the 100 disks would have a leading digit of 1, 10 a leading digit of 2,..., 10 a leading digit of 9, and 10 a leading digit of 0, the probability of each of the numbers 1,2,...,9,0 is 10/100 = .1.

If, say, three-digit random numbers are needed, each pair of two-digit numbers in each row of Table 4.6 can be combined, and the second-digit of the second member of each pair ignored. For example, in the first row the first pair, 50 and 17, could be combined to yield the three-digit random number 501.

This procedure is justified on the assumption that the experiment consists of: 1) selecting one disk and recording both digits; 2) replacing this disk; 3) selecting a second disk

(which, because of replacement, could be the same disk selected in the first draw) and recording the first digit only; and
4) combining the two digits of the first number drawn with the
first digit of the second number to form a three-digit number.
Since, in the experimental box, there are 100 equally likely
possibilities for the first two-digit random number (this number must be 01,02,...,99, or 00) and, for each of these 100
possibilities, 10 equally likely possibilities for the first digit
of the second two-digit random number (this first digit must
be 1,2,...,9, or 0), then 100 × 10 = 1,000 equally likely three-
digit random numbers can be generated in this way. These
three-digit random numbers are equally likely because the
first two digits of any given number are no more or less
likely than the first two digits of any other number, and the
third digit of any given number is no more or less likely than
the third digit of any other number. Hence, each three-digit
random number will have a probability of 1/1,000 = .001.

Using this approach, the reader should be able to see how
Table 4.6 can be used to yield random numbers of any size
i.e., random numbers composed of any number of digits.

We are now ready to formulate and solve our inventory
control problem.

4.43 The Problem. A retailer sells a product which he purchases from a wholesaler. Table 4.7 shows how the retail demand for this product has fluctuated over the past year. At
the end of a day the retailer must decide whether he should
order more units of this product. The lead time, i.e., the
number of days between the placing of an order and the receipt
of that order, fluctuates. Table 4.8 shows this fluctuation in
lead time for the past year. As in the inventory problem described at the very beginning of Section 4.2, the retailer believes that seasonal, cyclical, trend, and irregular factors have
not influenced these fluctuations in demand and lead time.
Hence, the fluctuations shown in Tables 4.7 and 4.8 are caused,
essentially, by stochastic factors. The retailer believes that
these same factors will be operating next year.

Three types of inventory costs are associated with this
product. First, an order cost is incurred each time an order
is placed. This cost includes clerical and paper costs associated with the preparation, dispatching, and receipt of an order,

TABLE 4.7

RETAIL DEMAND, PAST YEAR

Number of Units Demanded Daily	Number of Days in Which Specified Demand Occurred
30 but under 50	29
50 but under 70	50
70 but under 90	65
90 but under 110	108
110 but under 130	54
130 but under 150	36
150 but under 170	18
	360

TABLE 4.8

LEAD TIME, PAST YEAR

Number of Days Between Placement and Receipt of Order (Lead Time)	Number of Orders for Which Specified Lead Time Occurred
2	5
3	8
4	20
5	10
6	7
	50

and may include a fixed delivery charge as well. This cost is constant, regardless of the size of the order (e.g., the clerical costs are the same whether a large or small order is placed).

A second type of inventory cost, called holding cost, is incurred for each unit of the product held in inventory for one day. This cost includes interest on the money tied up in inventory that day, and also includes depreciation, obsolescence, insurance, and warehousing costs associated with this product, all figured on a per diem basis. This cost is a constant amount per unit in inventory per day.

The third type of inventory cost, shortage cost, is incurred for each unit of the product that is demanded but unavailable on a given day. Since it is assumed that the customer will go elsewhere to purchase this product, this cost includes the amount of profit the firm would have made if this product were available when demanded (hence, it represents an opportunity cost), and it may also include an element to account for the possible loss of consumer goodwill (the customer may be un-happy when turned away empty-handed).

Assume that, for this retailer, order cost is $20 per order, that holding cost is $.10 per product unit per day (e.g., if 10 units are in inventory for one day the total holding cost is $1, and if 10 units are in inventory for two days it is $2) and that shortage cost is $4 per unit of the product demanded but un-available. Let C_O denote the total order cost over a period of time (C_O equals $20 times the number of orders placed over this time period), C_H denote the total holding cost over a per-iod of time [C_H equals .10 times the number of product-day units over this period; e.g., if, in a three-day period, 8 units are in stock at the end of the first day, 4 at the end of the sec-ond day, and 2 at the end of the third day, the total holding cost is $.10(8+4+2) = $1.40], C_S denote the total shortage cost over a period of time (C_S equals $4 times the number of units de-manded but unavailable over this time period), and C_T denote total inventory cost over this period of time ($C_T = C_O + C_H + C_S$).

The term order quantity (denoted by Q) designates the fixed number of units ordered every time an order is placed, and the term order level (denoted by L) designates the level to which inventory at the end of the day is allowed to fall before an order is placed (if the actual inventory at the end of the day is less than or equal to L, an order is placed).

The decision problem facing the retailer is this: what values should he select for Q and L in order to minimize

$\underline{C}_T = \underline{C}_O + \underline{C}_H + \underline{C}_S$ for the coming year, when both demand and lead time are subject to the stochastic influences recorded in Tables 4.7 and 4.8?

4.44 Probability Distributions and Assigned Numbers. The data in Table 4.7 can be viewed as a summary of the outcomes of 360 empirical experiments. If we interpret these results as we did those of Table 4.1, we can use the midpoint of each class interval to represent that interval, and, hence, calculate the probabilities of the simple events "daily demand is 40 units", "daily demand is 60 units",..., "daily demand is 160 units" as 29/360 = .08, 50/360 = .14,..., 18/360 = .05. The first two columns of Table 4.9 show these results. [If we use random variable notation and terminology, then we would let $\underline{D}$ denote the identity random variable "daily demand", $\underline{x}$ denote the outcome of the experiment (the daily demand), $\underline{D}(\underline{x}) = \underline{x}$ denote the value of $\underline{D}$, and $\underline{P}(\underline{x}) = \underline{P}(\underline{d})$ denote the probability of the value $\underline{x} = \underline{d}$].

TABLE 4.9

PROBABILITY DISTRIBUTION FOR RETAIL DEMAND

$\underline{x} = \underline{d}$	$\underline{P}(\underline{x}) = \underline{P}(\underline{d})$	Assigned Numbers
40	.08	01 - 08
60	.14	09 - 22
80	.18	23 - 40
100	.30	41 - 70
120	.15	71 - 85
140	.10	86 - 95
160	.05	96 - 00
	1.00	

In a similar fashion, Table 4.8 can be viewed as a summary of the outcomes observed when a second empirical experiment was performed 50 times. The first two columns of Table 4.10 show the probabilities of the simple events defined for this experiment. [Using random variable notation, $\underline{T}$ denotes the identity random variable "lead time", $\underline{T}(\underline{x}) = \underline{x}$ denotes the value of $\underline{T}$ when the outcome of the experiment is $\underline{x}$, and $\underline{P}(\underline{x}) = \underline{P}(\underline{t})$ denotes the probability of the value $\underline{x} = \underline{t}$].

TABLE 4.10

PROBABILITY DISTRIBUTION FOR LEAD TIME

$\underline{x} = \underline{t}$	$\underline{P}(\underline{x}) = \underline{P}(\underline{t})$	Assigned Numbers
2 days	.10	01 - 10
3 days	.16	11 - 26
4 days	.40	27 - 66
5 days	.20	67 - 86
6 days	.14	87 - 00
	1.00	

The distinctive feature of Monte Carlo models is the simulation of these probability distributions by means of random numbers. The first step in this procedure is to assign ordinary (non-random) numbers to the simple events (the different values of the random variables) in Tables 4.9 and 4.10. The set of numbers assigned to a given event will be chosen so that the probability of obtaining one of these numbers in the box experiment described earlier is the same as the probability of the given event occurring in the demand experiment. Moreover, the same number cannot be assigned to more than one event.

For example, in Table 4.9, the event $\underline{D} = 40$ has probability $\underline{P}(\underline{D} = 40) = .08$. If we perform the box experiment, and if this box contains 100 two-digit disks, then the probability of the multiple event "01,02,..., or 08 is drawn" will also occur with probability $8/100 = .08$. That is, the event $\underline{D} = 40$ in the demand experiment has the same probability as the event "01, 02,..., or 08 occurs" in the box experiment. Hence, we assign these eight two-digit numbers to the event $\underline{D} = 40$.

Next, we consider the event $\underline{D} = 60$ in Table 4.9. Since we have already assigned the numbers 01,02,..., 08 to the event $\underline{D} = 40$, our assignment of numbers to the event $\underline{D} = 60$ must

begin with 09. Since $\underline{P}(\underline{D}$ = 60) is .14, and since the probability
of one of the numbers 09,10,...,22 occurring in the box experi-
ment is .14, we assign these fourteen numbers to the event $\underline{D}$ =
40.

Proceeding in this manner, we assign the numbers 23,24,
...,99,00 to the remaining events in Table 4.9 (see column 3).
The assignment of numbers in Table 4.10 is made (column 3)
in exactly the same way. The reason for making these assign-
ments will become apparent in the next section. Note that if
the probabilities of the various events were in tenths or thou-
sandths, instead of hundredths, the numbers assigned would be
one-digit or three-digit numbers, respectively.

4.45   <u>Solution by Simulation.</u>   We are now ready to apply the
Monte Carlo simulation method to this problem. The first step
is to <u>arbitrarily</u> select what appear to be reasonable $\underline{Q}$ and $\underline{L}$
values. For example, assume the retailer decided to start the
analysis with the values $\underline{Q}$ = 800 and $\underline{L}$ = 500; i.e., every time
an order is placed, $\underline{Q}$ = 800 units will be ordered, and this order will be placed whenever the inventory at the end of a day
falls to a level of 500 or less. These particular $\underline{Q}$ and $\underline{L}$ values
represent just one possible starting combination. Before the
simulation analysis is completed, many other $\underline{Q}$ - $\underline{L}$ combinations will be tried. The particular combination leading to the
best simulated results will be the one the retailer will actually
implement in the real world.

Given the values initially assumed for $\underline{Q}$ and $\underline{L}$ and the
values previously specified for order, holding, and shortage
costs, we shall simulate, in Table 4.11, the operation of this
system for 20 days. That is, we shall employ the data and
concepts introduced to predict what might occur if we were
actually to implement a decision of $\underline{Q}$ = 800 and $\underline{L}$ = 500 in
the real world for 20 days.

To start the simulation, we assume a beginning inventory
equal to the order quantity $\underline{Q}$ = 800. We do not know exactly
what the actual demand will be during the first day, but we do
know the probabilities of the various possibilities. To simulate demand on the first day (to determine what demand might
actually be in the real world), we perform a box experiment
(select the first number in Table 4.6). This number, 50, is recorded in column 2 of Table 4.11. Table 4.9 shows that the

TABLE 4.11

20 DAYS SIMULATION WITH Q = 800, L = 500

(1)	(2)	(3)	(4)	(5)	(6)	(7)	(8)	(9)	(10)	(11)	(12)
	Random No. for		Begin.			End.	Ld.				
Day	Dem.	Ld. Tme.	Inv.	Receipts	Dem.	Inv.	Tme.	C_O	C_H	C_S	C_T
1	50	——	800	0	100	700	——	0	70	0	70
2	72	——	700	0	120	580	——	0	58	0	58
3	56	82	580	0	100	480	5	20	48	0	68
4	48	——	480	0	100	380	——	0	38	0	38
5	09	——	380	0	60	320	——	0	32	0	32
6	01	——	320	0	40	280	——	0	28	0	28
7	91	——	280	0	140	140	——	0	14	0	14
8	24	——	140	800	80	860	——	0	86	0	86
9	24	——	860	0	80	780	——	0	78	0	78
10	17	——	780	0	60	720	——	0	72	0	72
11	22	——	720	0	60	660	——	0	66	0	66
12	57	——	660	0	100	560	——	0	56	0	56
13	82	88	560	0	120	440	6	20	44	0	64
14	54	——	440	0	100	340	——	0	34	0	34
15	50	——	340	0	100	240	——	0	24	0	24
16	98	——	240	0	160	80	——	0	8	0	8
17	41	——	80	0	100	0	——	0	0	80	80
18	94	——	0	0	140	0	——	0	0	560	560
19	33	——	0	800	80	720	——	0	72	0	72
20	21	——	720	0	60	660	——	0	66	0	66
	Total for 20 days							40	894	640	1574
	Average for 20 days (C_O, C_H, C_S, C_T)							2	45	32	79

numbers 41 to 70 are associated with a demand of 100 units.
Since our first random number falls in this range, we take 100
units as the demand in the first day, and record it in column 6
of Table 4.11.

This procedure is justified because, in constructing Table
4.9, we assigned all possible two-digit numbers to the possible
simple events in the demand experiment. Since there are seven
possible simple events, we had to place all the possible two-
digit numbers into seven different sets. That is, we really assigned seven sets of numbers to the seven simple events. The
numbers were so allocated that the probability of obtaining any
given set equalled exactly the probability of the event to which
it corresponded. Now, when we actually perform the box experiment, we do not know which random number will occur;
similarly, during any given demand experiment we do not know
which demand will actually occur. Chance alone determines
which random number, and which demand, will occur. However, since the probability of obtaining each set of numbers in
the box experiment is the same as the probability of obtaining

the demand to which it corresponds, we can simulate the actual experience with the box experiments. (Note that in applying the Monte Carlo method it is never necessary to actually perform box experiments; as we noted in Section 4.42, in effect, these experiments have already been performed by others and the results published in tables.)

Continuing with our first day's simulation, we compute ending inventory as beginning inventory plus receipts minus demand (i.e., 800 + 0 - 100 = 700). The only inventory cost incurred this day is a holding cost equal to the ending inventory (700) times $.10. The beginning inventory for the second day is the ending inventory of the preceding day. The second day's demand is simulated by drawing the random number 72 which, from Table 4.9, corresponds to a demand of 120 units.

In the third day, the random number 56 occurs. The corresponding demand of 100 units brings the ending inventory this day below L = 500. Hence, an order is placed this day. To find out when this order will arrive, we obtain the next random number, 82, and refer to Table 4.10. We see that the number 82 implies a lead time of 5 days. Hence, since the order is placed in the third day, it will be received in the third plus five, or eighth, day. We assume that orders are available for sale at the beginning of the day on which they are received (note the order quantity 800 in row 8 and column 5 of Table 4.11). Since an order was placed this day, we record a 20 dollar order cost in column 9.

The reader should be able to find his way through the table. Notice that on the 17th day, 100 units are demanded but only 80 are available, so that a shortage cost of $4(20) = $80 is incurred; on the 18th day an additional shortage of $4(140) = $560 is incurred.

The bottom line of Table 4.11 shows that, on the average, the daily inventory costs for Q = 800 and L = 500 are $\bar{C}_O$ = 2, $\bar{C}_H$ = 45, $\bar{C}_S$ = 32, and $\bar{C}_T$ = 79 where the bar over the symbol denotes the arithmetic mean of the quantity in question.

In practice, 20 simulations of a given Q - L combination will not be sufficient to determine its effectiveness. How many simulations are necessary? The answer to this question depends on the particular problem being simulated. One way to approach it would be to compute the average costs $\bar{C}_O$, $\bar{C}_H$,

$\underline{\bar{C}}_S$ and $\underline{\bar{C}}_T$, every, say, 100 simulations, and continue the simulations until these averages stabilize.[3]   For example, in the present problem, 900 simulations were carried out[4] and the results summarized in Table 4.12. It appears that 600 simulations is about the right number in this problem.[5]

TABLE 4.12

BEHAVIOR OF $\underline{\bar{C}}_O$, $\underline{\bar{C}}_H$, $\underline{\bar{C}}_S$, AND $\underline{\bar{C}}_T$

OVER 900 SIMULATIONS

Simulation Number	$\underline{\bar{C}}_O$	$\underline{\bar{C}}_H$	$\underline{\bar{C}}_S$	$\bar{C}_T$
100	2.40	51.00	.24	53.64
200	2.40	51.50	.20	54.10
300	2.40	51.04	.18	53.62
400	2.35	52.28	.20	54.83
500	2.36	52.42	.16	54.94
600	2.33	53.36	.13	55.82
700	2.31	53.56	.11	55.98
800	2.32	53.58	.10	56.00
900	2.31	53.40	.26	55.97

Now that we know that a total inventory cost of about $56 per day on the average (Table 4.12) is associated with the decision to set $\underline{Q}$ = 800 and $\underline{L}$ = 500, we have to compare this result with the results generated by other $\underline{Q}$ - $\underline{L}$ combinations.

---

[3] In some systems, the averages may explode. But this will become evident and typically, corrective measures can be readily undertaken.

[4] These simulations were run by the author on an IBM 1620 computer. Graduate assistants Charles Olivieri and Ronald Bleakney should receive credit for their considerable effort in debugging the author's original program.

[5] As Table 4.12 shows, $\overline{\underline{C}}_T$ stabilizes at about $56 after 600 simulations. Even after 100 simulations, $\overline{\underline{C}}_T$ is not significantly different from this value.

Table 4.13 shows the results for 25 Q - L combinations in which Q ranges from 600 to 1,000 and L from 300 to 700, both in intervals of 100. 900 simulations were run[6] for each combination. We notice that the combination yielding the lowest average $\bar{C}_T$ (equal to $49) is Q = 600 and L = 500. Using this result we could zero in closer on the best combination by letting Q range from 500 to 700 and L from 400 to 600, both in intervals of, say, 50. Proceeding in this way, we will eventually arrive at a "best" decision for Q and L.

TABLE 4.13

$\bar{C}_T$ FOR 25 Q - L COMBINATIONS

Q	300	400	500	600	700
600	69	51	49	57	66
700	63	54	53	60	70
800	70	56	56	65	75
900	70	61	63	70	80
1000	71	64	67	74	87

The procedure just described would, in general, be too cumbersome and time-consuming to implement by hand calculations. However, by using an electronic digital computer, the problem just treated can be solved in a matter of minutes.[7]

We chose to illustrate Monte Carlo simulation by means of an inventory control problem. However, this method can and has[8] been used to solve all kinds of management decision

---

[6] See footnote 4.

[7] On an IBM 1620 computer, 900 simulations of a given Q-L combination takes about 4 minutes.

[8] For example, see O.J. Feorene, "The Gentle Art of Simulation", Proceedings, Twelfth Annual Industrial Engineering Institute, University of California, Berkeley-Los Angeles, 1960; H.G. Jones and A.M.Lee, "Monte Carlo Methods in Heavy Industry", Operations Research Quarterly, Vol. VI, No. 3; C. McMillan and R.F. Gonzalez, Systems Analysis (Homewood, Ill.: Richard D. Irwin, Inc., 1965, Chs. 6,9); and R. Neate and W.J. Dacey, "A Simulation of a Melting Shop Operation by Means of a Computer", Process Control and Automation, Vol. V, No. 7, July 1958.

problems. Hence, it is a very general, and extremely useful, management technique.

4.5   DISCUSSION AND REVIEW QUESTIONS

1. Distinguish between the expected profit of the best decision under uncertainty and the expected profit with perfect information. How are these two concepts related to the value of perfect information?

2. In Section 4.25, if all of the expected value computations were negative, what would be the optimum standing order?

3. When can Monte Carlo models be applied and what are their advantages?

4. Why is the Monte Carlo method a trial and error procedure?

5. What is the role of random numbers in Monte Carlo simulation?

6. How do you know when a sufficient number of simulations has been performed?

4.6   EXERCISES

1. In the problem described in Section 4.2, assume the price of a loaf of bread is $.40 instead of $.30.

    (a) Determine the optimum standing order.
    (b) Determine the expected profit with perfect information.
    (c) Determine the value of perfect information.

2. Assume that Table 4.14 summarizes the daily demand for milk over the past year in a given supermarket. Assume, further, that the price per quart is $.20 and the cost $.18. Assume, finally, that milk ordered but not sold at the end of the day can be returned to the supplier with a rebate of $.05 per quart.

TABLE 4.14

DAILY DEMAND FOR MILK, PAST YEAR

Number of Quarts Demanded Daily	Number of Days in Which the Stated Number of Quarts Was Demanded
400 but under 600	20
600 but under 800	40
800 but under 1,000	90
1,000 but under 1,200	100
1,200 but under 1,400	80
1,400 but under 1,600	20
	350

(a) What is the optimum standing order?
(b) What is the expected profit with perfect informa-tion?
(c) What is the value of perfect information?

3. Extend Table 4.11 through 50 days of simulation and then compute $\underline{C}_O$, $\underline{C}_H$, $\underline{C}_S$, and $\underline{C}_T$.

4. In Section 4.44, we assumed that units demanded but unavailable represented a $4 shortage cost per unit, and that the customer would go elsewhere to satisfy his demand. Now change this assumption, so that: 1) the shortage cost is $4 per unit per day short, and 2) when an order comes in, back orders are filled first. As this implies, customers do not go elsewhere for this product, but wait until it comes in. Moreover, the firm pays a $4 penalty fee for each day a unit is short [e.g., if 10 units are demanded by a customer but are unavailable, and if delivery is made 3 days later, the shortage cost incurred for this customer is $4 (10)(3) = $120]. In this case, simulate 50 days, drawing your random numbers from the beginning of Table 4.6.

5. A financial analyst is able to prepare the information given in Table 4.15. Simulate the cash flows for 20 weeks, and determine the cumulative cash balance at the end of each week, assuming an initial balance of $5,000.

TABLE 4.15

MONTHLY CASH FLOW PROBABILITIES

Monthly Cash Inflow ($\underline{x}$)	$\underline{P}(\underline{x})$	Monthly Cash Outflow ($\underline{y}$)	$\underline{P}(\underline{y})$
$1,000	.1	$1,000	.05
1,500	.1	1,500	.10
2,000	.3	1,800	.30
2,500	.3	2,200	.55
3,000	.2		

6. Table 4.16 shows a firm's probability distributions for monthly cash sales and credit sales. Table 4.17 shows the probability distribution for the percentage of the preceding month's accounts receivable which will be collected in the current month. Assume that the retail value of beginning inventory is $14,000. At the end of each month inventories are brought back up to this retail level of $14,000; since the mark-up on each item is 20 percent of the selling price, purchases at the end of each month will be 80 percent of that month's total sales. These purchases are paid in full at the end of the next month. Cash balance at the beginning of the period of analysis is $4,000. Every third month cash dividends of $500 are paid. Use the headings which follow as the basis of a Monte Carlo simulation table for the financial analysis of this firm over the next 12 months: Month, Random Number for Cash Sales, Cash Sales, Random Number for Credit Sales, Credit Sales, Total Sales, Random Number for Percentage of Preceding Month's Accounts Receivable Collected, Percentage of Preceding Month's Accounts Receivable Collected, Preceding Month's Accounts Receivable Collected, Total Cash Inflow, Purchases, Dividends, Total Cash Outflow, Beginning Cash Balance, Ending Cash Balance, Accounts Receivable, Accounts Payable, Acid Test Ratio.

TABLE 4.16

PROBABILITIES FOR MONTHLY
CASH AND CREDIT SALES

Monthly Cash Sales ($\underline{x}$)	$\underline{P}(\underline{x})$	Monthly Credit Sales ($\underline{y}$)	$\underline{P}(\underline{y})$
$1,000	.70	$5,000	.1
2,000	.10	6,000	.2
3,000	.08	7,000	.3
4,000	.07	8,000	.3
5,000	.05	9,000	.1

TABLE 4.17

CREDIT-PAYMENT PERCENTAGES
AND THEIR PROBABILITIES

Percentage of Preceding Month's Accounts Receivable Collected in Current Month ($\underline{z}$)	$P(\underline{z})$
.1	.10
.2	.20
.3	.40
.4	.20
.5	.10

5 ▶   SOME PROBABILITY THEOREMS AND THE BINOMIAL PROBABILITY DISTRIBUTION

5.1   MOTIVATION

In this chapter we shall prove several important theorems from the theory of probability. We shall also describe a very important type of stochastic experiment, called a binomial experiment. We shall then define a binomial random variable and show how to construct the associated binomial probability distribution. This distribution has very many applications in business, and the succeeding chapters will describe some of them.

However, before beginning our study of these concepts, it will be necessary to develop the basic mathematical concept of permutations.

5.2   PERMUTATIONS

A permutation of n objects r $(r \leq n)$ at a time is a distinct arrangement of r objects selected from the n objects. By "distinct arrangement" we mean an arrangement which is no - ticeably different from any other arrangement that might be formed. For example, if we have the n = 3 letters A, B, and C, one permutation (distinct arrangement) of r = 2 of these objects (letters) is BC; a second is AB; a third is AC and so on.

Interest centers on the number of permutations that can be formed when r objects are selected from n objects. We shall consider two cases. In the first case, each of the n objects is noticeably different. In the second case, some of the n objects are identical.

5.21   Formula for Ordinary Permutations. Assume we have n ob - jects, each of which is noticeably different. A permutation formed from r $(r \leq n)$ of these n objects will be called an ordi - nary permutation. Assume that we wish to find the number of ordinary permutations possible when r $(r \leq n)$ of these objects are selected. The first position in the permutation can be filled by any one of n objects. Once this object has been selected, the second position can be filled by any one of the remaining $n - 1$ objects. Since there are n ways of filling the first position, and, for each of these, $n - 1$ ways of filling the second position, there are $n(n-1)$ ways of filling the first two positions.

Now, once the first two positions have been filled, there are $n - 2$ choices left for the third position. Since the first two po - sitions can be filled in $n(n-1)$ different ways, and since, for each of these ways, the third position can be filled in $n - 2$ ways, there are $[n(n-1)](n-2)$ = $n(n-1)(n-2)$ ways of filling the first three positions.

To proceed one step further, once the first three positions in the permutation have been filled, there are $n - 3$ objects left from which to choose the fourth position. Since the first three positions can be filled in $n(n-1)(n-2)$ different ways, and since, for each of these ways, the fourth position can be filled in $n - 3$ ways, there are $[n(n-1)(n-2)](n-3)$ = $n(n-1)(n-2)(n-3)$ ways of filling the first four positions.

Let $\underline{G}(\underline{r},\underline{n})$ denote the total number of ordinary permutations possible when $\underline{r}$ objects are selected from $\underline{n}$ objects. Then from the preceding discussion, we have shown that $\underline{G}(1,\underline{n}) = \underline{n}$, $\underline{G}(2,\underline{n}) = \underline{n}(\underline{n}-1)$, $\underline{G}(3,\underline{n}) = \underline{n}(\underline{n}-1)(\underline{n}-2)$, and $\underline{G}(4,\underline{n}) = \underline{n}(\underline{n}-1)(\underline{n}-2)(\underline{n}-3)$. Notice in each case that the number of factors after the equal sign is equal to $\underline{r}$, that the first factor is $\underline{n}$ and each succeeding factor decreases by 1, and that the last factor is always $(\underline{n}-\underline{r}+1)$.

From these results, the reader should be able to verify the following general formula for ordinary permutations:

$$\underline{G}(\underline{r},\underline{n}) = \underline{n}(\underline{n}-1)(\underline{n}-2) \ldots (\underline{n}-\underline{r}+1) \qquad (5.1)$$

Note that $\underline{r}$ can never be greater than $\underline{n}$ (why?).

As an illustration, take the 3 letters $\underline{A}$, $\underline{B}$, $\underline{C}$. The number of ordinary permutations of $\underline{r} = 2$ of these $\underline{n} = 3$ objects can be determined by enumeration: $\underline{AB}$, $\underline{AC}$, $\underline{BA}$, $\underline{BC}$, $\underline{CA}$, $\underline{CB}$. Thus 6 ordinary permutations are possible. Eq. 5.1 also yields $\underline{G}(2,3) = 3(2) = 6$. The number of permutations of $\underline{r} = 3$ of these $\underline{n} = 3$ objects is seen, by enumeration, to be 6: $\underline{ABC}$, $\underline{ACB}$, $\underline{BAC}$, $\underline{BCA}$, $\underline{CAB}$, $\underline{CBA}$. Eq. 5.1 also yields $\underline{G}(3,3) = 3(2)(1) = 6$.

If we wanted to find the number of permutations of $\underline{r} = 3$ letters taken from the $\underline{n} = 4$ letters $\underline{A}$, $\underline{B}$, $\underline{C}$, and $\underline{D}$, we could use Eq. 5.1 and obtain $\underline{G}(3,4) = 4(3)(2) = 24$. The reader can verify this by enumeration.

Eq. 5.1 is more convenient if transformed into an equivalent expression. Let the product $\underline{n}(\underline{n}-1)(\underline{n}-2) \ldots 1$ ($\underline{n}$ is an integer) be denoted by $\underline{n}!$ (read "n factorial"). $\underline{n}!$ is thus a product of $\underline{n}$ factors, the first being $\underline{n}$, each succeeding factor being 1 less than the preceding factor, and the last factor being 1. For example, $3! = 3(2)(1) = 6$, $4! = 4(3)(2)(1) = 24$, and $5! = 5(4)(3)(2)(1) = 120$. By definition $0! = 1$.

An equivalent expression for Eq. 5.1 is given by

$$\underline{G}(\underline{r},n) = \underline{n}!/(\underline{n}-\underline{r})! \qquad (5.2)$$

Eq. 5.2 is valid since

$$\underline{n}!/(\underline{n}-\underline{r})! = [\underline{n}(\underline{n}-1)(\underline{n}-2) \ldots (\underline{n}-\underline{r}+1)(\underline{n}-\underline{r})(\underline{n}-\underline{r}-1) \ldots 1] /$$
$$[(\underline{n}-\underline{r})(\underline{n}-\underline{r}-1) \ldots 1]$$
$$= \underline{n}(\underline{n}-1)(\underline{n}-2) \ldots (\underline{n}-\underline{r}+1) = \underline{G}(\underline{r},\underline{n})$$

For example, using Eq. 5.2 we obtain $\underline{G}(2,4) = [4(3)(2)(1)]/[2(1)] = 12$, $\underline{G}(4,4) = [4(3)(2)(1)]/0! = [4(3)(2)(1)]/1 = 24$ and

$\underline{G}(4,7) = [7(6)(5)\ldots 1]/[3(2)(1)] = 840$. The reader can
verify these results by using Eq. 5.1.

5.22 Formula for Two-Category Permutations. Assume we have
$\underline{n}$ objects, $\underline{s}$ of which are of one kind and $\underline{n} - \underline{s}$ of which are of
a second kind. A permutation formed from $\underline{r} = \underline{n}$ of these $\underline{n}$
objects will be called a two-category permutation. For ex-
ample, the $\underline{n} = 5$ letters $\underline{A}, \underline{A}, \underline{B}, \underline{B}$, and $\underline{B}$ represent two different kinds of objects: $\underline{s} = 2$ $\underline{A}$'s, and $\underline{n}-\underline{s} = 3$ $\underline{B}$'s. We wish to
determine the number of two-category permutations possible
from $\underline{n}$ objects, $\underline{s}$ of one kind and $\underline{n}-\underline{s}$ of a second kind. Let
$\underline{D}(\underline{s},\underline{n})$ denote this number.

Consider a given two-category permutation of the $\underline{n}$ ob-
jects, $\underline{s}$ of one kind and $\underline{n}-\underline{s}$ of a second kind. If the $\underline{s}$ objects
of the first kind were actually noticeably different, this single
two-category permutation could be expanded to $\underline{s}!$ permutations. This follows because the position occupied by the first
of the $\underline{s}$ objects could be filled in $\underline{s}$ ways, the position occupied
by the second of the $\underline{s}$ objects in $\underline{s}-1$ ways, etc., so that these
same $\underline{s}$ positions could be filled in $\underline{s}(\underline{s}-1)\ldots 1$ different ways.

For example, given the distinguishable permutation
$\underline{ABBABAB}$ (where $\underline{n} = 7$, $\underline{s} = 3$, $\underline{n} - s = 4$), if the 3 $\underline{A}$'s were
noticeably different, the $\underline{A}$ in the first position of this permu-
tation could be filled in any one of three ways, for each of
these the $\underline{A}$ in the fourth position could be filled in any one of
two ways, and for each of these $3(2) = 6$ ways the $\underline{A}$ in the sixth
position could be filled in 1 way. If we use subscripts to de-
note these different $\underline{A}$'s, we see that $\underline{s}! = 3! = 6$ permutations
will result: $\underline{A_1 BBA_2 BA_3 B}$, $\underline{A_1 BBA_3 BA_2 B}$, $\underline{A_2 BBA_1 BA_3 B}$,
$\underline{A_2 BBA_3 BA_1 B}$, $\underline{A_3 BBA_1 BA_2 B}$, $\underline{A_3 BBA_2 BA_1 B}$.

Similarly, if the $\underline{n}-\underline{s}$ objects of the second kind were actually noticeably different, this single two-category permutation
could give rise to $(\underline{n}-\underline{s})!$ permutations. Moreover, if both the
$\underline{s}$ objects of the first kind and the $\underline{n}-\underline{s}$ objects of the second kind
were noticeably different, this single two-category permutation
could be expanded to $\underline{s}!(\underline{n}-\underline{s})!$ ordinary permutations. This follows because for each of the $\underline{s}!$ permutations generated by the
first kind of object, $(\underline{n}-\underline{s})!$ permutations can be formed from
the second kind of object.

Since there are $\underline{D}(\underline{s},\underline{n})$ two-category permutations, and
since each such permutation can generate $\underline{s}!(\underline{n}-\underline{s})!$ ordinary

permutations, the set of two-category permutations can thus generate $\underline{D}(\underline{s},\underline{n})\underline{s}!(\underline{n}-\underline{s})!$ ordinary permutations. But the number of ordinary permutations[1] is $\underline{G}(\underline{n},\underline{n})$. That is

$$\underline{G}(\underline{n},\underline{n}) = \underline{D}(\underline{s},\underline{n})\underline{s}!(\underline{n}-\underline{s})!$$

or

$$\underline{D}(\underline{s},\underline{n}) = \underline{G}(\underline{n},\underline{n})/[\underline{s}!(\underline{n}-\underline{s})!] = [\underline{n}!/(\underline{n}-\underline{n})!]/[\underline{s}!(\underline{n}-\underline{s})!]$$

$$= \underline{n}!/[\underline{s}!(\underline{n}-\underline{s})!] \tag{5.3}$$

Thus, using Eq. 5.3, the number of two-category permutations possible from 3 $\underline{A}$'s and 4 $\underline{B}$'s is $7!/(3!4!) = 35$. To take an illustration which can be quickly verified by enumeration, consider the $\underline{n} = 3$ letters $\underline{A}, \underline{A},$ and $\underline{B}$. Eq. 5.3 indicates that $3!/(2!1!) = 3$ distinguishable permutations are possible. By enumeration we easily see that these are $\underline{AAB}, \underline{ABA},$ and $\underline{BAA}$.

The concept of two-category permutations will be needed when we introduce the binomial probability distribution. But first it will be necessary to develop several probability theorems.

5.3   ADDITION THEOREM

We have defined an event as a set of one or more of the possible outcomes in an experiment   A simple event contains exactly one outcome while a multiple event contains more than one outcome. In this section, we shall be concerned with determining the probability that any one of two or more events will occur in an experiment. Two cases can arise. In the first case, the events are mutually exclusive; in the second case, they are not. We shall consider the first case only.

---

[1]The reader now should be able to generalize Eq. 5.3 to the case where there are $\underline{s}_t (\underline{t} > 2)$ kinds of objects ($\underline{s}_1 + \underline{s}_2 + ... + \underline{s}_t = \underline{n}$). We shall only use the two-category case in this book.

5.31   Mutually Exclusive Events. Two or more events defined for a given experiment are mutually exclusive if none of the events contains an outcome that is also associated with one of the other events. For example, if a die is tossed, the event "the number of spots is 5 or more" and the event "the number of spots is 3 or less" are mutually exclusive. The former event contains the outcomes 5 and 6 and the latter event the outcomes 1, 2, and 3; none of the outcomes associated with the first event are also associated with the second. However, the events "the number of spots is 3 or less" and "the number of spots is 2 or more" are not mutually exclusive, since they both contain the outcomes 2 and 3.

In general, let x_1, x_2, . . ., x_n denote the list of collectively exhaustive and mutually exclusive outcomes in an a priori experiment. Let E_1 and E_2 denote two mutually exclusive events defined for these outcomes. Specifically, let the outcomes x_1, x_2, and x_3 be associated with E_1, and let x_4 and x_8 be associated with E_2. If we let n_1 and n_2 denote, respectively, the number of outcomes associated with E_1 and E_2, we see that $n_1 = 3$ and $n_2 = 2$. From Definition 2.1, we know that the probability of E_1 occurring is $P(E_1) = n_1/n$ and the probability of E_2 occurring is $P(E_2) = n_2/n$. Moreover, the probability of either E_1 or E_2 occurring is $P(E_1 \lor E_2) = (n_1 + n_2)/n = (n_1/n) + (n_2/n) = P(E_1) + P(E_2)$.

In general, if m mutually exclusive events $E_1, E_2, . . . E_m$ are defined for this a priori experiment, and if the number of outcomes associated with each event is given by $n_1, n_2, . . . n_m$, respectively, then the probability of any one of these events occurring in a single experiment is $P(E_1 \lor E_2 \lor . . . \lor E_m) =$
$(n_1 + n_2 + . . . + n_m)/n = (n_1/n) + (n_2/n) + . . . + (n_m/n)$

or

$$P(E_1 \lor E_2 \lor . . . \lor E_m) = P(E_1) + P(E_2) + . . . + P(E_m) \quad (5.4)$$

Eq. 5.4 is known as the addition theorem for mutually exclusive events. It gives the probability of any one of two or more mutually exclusive events occurring in a single experiment.

To return to a previous example, if a single die is tossed, the probability of the event E_1 "3 or less spots turn up" is $3/6 = .50$ and the probability of the event E_2 "5 or more spots turn up" is $2/6 = .33$. Therefore, $P(E_1 \lor E_2) = P(E_1) + P(E_2) = .50 + .33 = .83$.

While Eq. 5.4 was derived with reference to a priori experiments, it also holds exactly for empirical and subjective experiments. To illustrate, let an empirical experiment have the outcomes $x_1, x_2, \ldots, x_n$. In a large number of experiments, say N, assume these outcomes occurred, respectively, $n_1, n_2, \ldots, n_n$ times. Let E_1 and E_2 be multiple events which are also mutually exclusive. Assume E_1 contains the outcomes x_1 and x_2, and E_2 the outcomes x_3, x_6, and x_8. Then, from Definition 2.2, the probability of either E_1 or E_2 occurring on the next experiment is $P(E_1 \vee E_2) = (n_1 + n_2 + n_3 + n_6 + n_8)/N = [(n_1 + n_2)/(N)] + [(n_3 + n_6 + n_8)/N] = (P(E_1) + P(E_2))$. This result is entirely consistent with Eq. 5.4 . The reader can readily generalize it to m events. Moreover, if the subjective probabilities of simple events are interpreted as the relative frequencies which will likely result if many (say N) experiments are performed, the same analysis just given can be applied to derive Eq. 5.4.

As an example, if .05 is the probability of the multiple event E_1 "demand is 2 or 3 units" and .10 the probability of E_2 "demand is 4 or 5 units", then $P(E_1 \vee E_2) = P(E_1) + P(E_2) = .05 + .10 = .15$.

5.4   MULTIPLICATION THEOREM FOR INDEPENDENT EVENTS

Up to now we have considered the probability of an event occurring in a single experiment. Now we shall consider the probability of each of two or more events occurring in a series of two or more experiments.

5.41   Compound Experiments and Events.

Whenever we are interested in the results of two or more separate experiments performed in succession, we shall refer to the series of experiments as a compound experiment. The sequence of events that is observed when a compound experiment is performed will be called a compound event. Each separate experiment making up a compound experiment will be called a basic experiment. The event observed in a basic experiment will be called a basic event.

For example, assume we have two boxes. The first box
contains 3 white golf balls and 3 black golf balls, and the second box contains 2 white, 4 black, and 4 green golf balls. A
compound experiment consists of drawing one ball from the
first box (the first basic experiment) and one ball from the
second box (the second basic experiment). The sequence of two
colors observed is a compound event. The color obtained
from the first box is the first basic event, and the color from
the second box is the second basic event.

5.42   Independent Events.   In a compound experiment, if the
probability of any given basic event occurring on any given
basic experiment is in no way affected by the outcomes of any
of the other preceding basic experiments making up the compound experiment, we say that the basic experiments and the
basic events are independent. For example, in the box compound experiment cited in the preceding section, the probability of the basic event "white ball" occurring on the second basic experiment is $2/10$ = .2 regardless of the event observed in the first basic experiment. Thus the two basic
events are independent.

5.43   General Formula.   We now shall derive a general formula
for the probability of a compound event made up of independent
basic events. Let two basic a priori experiments be performed.
Assume these experiments are independent. Let N_1 and N_2 denote the total number of possible outcomes in each experiment,
respectively. Let E_1 denote a basic event defined for the first
experiment and E_2 a basic event defined for the second experiment. E_1 and E_2 are independent events. Let n_1 and n_2 denote,
respectively, the number of outcomes in the first and second
experiments contained in E_1 and E_2 . Now, the total number of
possible compound outcomes [2] is $N_1(N_2)$. Of these $N_1(N_2)$ possible compound outcomes, $n_1(n_2)$ compound outcomes correspond to the events E_1 on the first experiment and E_2 on the
second. These compound outcomes are equally likely, and hence
(from Definition 2.1) the probability of the compound event $E_1 E_2$

---

[2] A compound outcome is one of the possible results of the compound experiment.

is $\underline{P}(\underline{E}_1 \& \underline{E}_2) = (\underline{n}_1 \underline{n}_2)/(\underline{N}_1 \underline{N}_2) = (\underline{n}_1/\underline{N}_1)(\underline{n}_2/\underline{N}_2) = \underline{P}(\underline{E}_1)\underline{P}(\underline{E}_2)$. Thus, the probability of each of two independent basic events occurring in succession is the product of their separate probabilities, i.e., the product of the probabilities of each occurring in its basic experiment.

For example, assume the first basic experiment involves drawing at random a ball from a box containing 3 white and 3 black balls, and the second basic experiment involves drawing a ball from a second box containing 2 white, 4 black, and 4 green balls. Let $\underline{E}_1$ be "a white ball" and $\underline{E}_2$ "a black ball". The probabilities of these basic events (the separate probabilities) are $\underline{P}(\underline{E}_1) = 3/6 = .5$ and $\underline{P}(\underline{E}_2) = 4/10 = .4$. We also have $\underline{N}_1 = 6$, $\underline{N}_2 = 10$, $\underline{n}_1 = 3$, and $\underline{n}_2 = 4$. For each of the 6 outcomes possible on the first basic experiment there are 10 outcomes possible on the second, so that $\underline{N}_1(\underline{N}_2) = 6(10) = 60$ compound outcomes are possible. Of these 60 outcomes, $\underline{n}_1(\underline{n}_2) = 3(4) = 12$ yield the compound event $\underline{E}_1\underline{E}_2$ or "a white followed by a black ball". Thus $\underline{P}(\underline{E}_1 \& \underline{E}_2) = [3(4)]/[6(10)] = (3/6)(4/10) = \underline{P}(\underline{E}_1)\underline{P}(\underline{E}_2) = .5(.4) = .2$.

The reader should now be ready to generalize this result for compound events made up of two independent basic events to compound events made up of any number of independent basic events. Assume we perform $\underline{m}$ independent basic experiments, and are interested in the occurrence of the event $\underline{E}_1$ on the first basic experiment, $\underline{E}_2$ on the second, . . . , and $\underline{E}_{\underline{m}}$ on the mth basic experiment. Let $\underline{n}_{\underline{i}}$ ($\underline{i} = 1, 2, . . ., \underline{m}$) denote the number of outcomes in each experiment contained in event $\underline{E}_{\underline{i}}$. Then the probability of each of the $\underline{m}$ events occurring when the $\underline{m}$ basic experiments are performed, i.e., the probability of the compound event composed of these $\underline{m}$ basic events, is determined from the product of their separate probabilities:

$$\underline{P}(\underline{E}_1 \& \underline{E}_2 \& . . . \& \underline{E}_{\underline{m}}) = (\underline{n}_1 \underline{n}_2 . . . \underline{n}_{\underline{m}})/(\underline{N}_1 \underline{N}_2 . . . \underline{N}_{\underline{m}})$$
$$= (\underline{n}_1/\underline{N}_1)(\underline{n}_2/\underline{N}_2) . . . (\underline{n}_{\underline{m}}/\underline{N}_{\underline{m}})$$
$$= \underline{P}(\underline{E}_1)\underline{P}(\underline{E}_2) . . . \underline{P}(\underline{E}_{\underline{m}}) \qquad (5.5)$$

Eq. 5.5 is known as the multiplication theorem for independent events.

We derived Eq. 5.5 from an a priori compound experiment, but it holds exactly for empirical and subjective experiments as well. Assume that a compound experiment is performed a great many, say N, times. This compound experiment is made up of two independent basic empirical experiments. Thus, both basic experiments are performed in succession N times. Let n_1 denote the number of times event E_1 occurred in the first experiment, n_2 the number of times E_2 occurred in the second experiment, and $n_{1,2}$ the number of times E_2 occurred in the second experiment when E_1 also occurred in the first experiment (note that $n_{1,2} \leq n_1$).

Let $P(E_2 \mid E_1)$ denote the probability (called a conditional probability) that E_2 occurs (in the second experiment) given the information that E_1 has already occurred (in the first experiment). From Definition 2.2, we know that $P(E_2 \mid E_1) = n_{1,2}/n_1$. But since the events E_1 and E_2 are independent, the probability of E_2 occurring is really in no way affected by the outcome of the first experiment. That is, $P(E_2 \mid E_1)$ simply equals the probability $P(E_2)$ that E_2 will occur on the second experiment. Since $P(E_2) = n_2/N$, we thus have $P(E_2 \mid E_1) = n_{1,2}/n_1 = P(E_2) = n_2/N$ or $n_{1,2}(N) = n_1(n_2)$. Dividing both sides of this expression by $N(N)$ we obtain $n_{1,2}/N = (n_1 n_2)/(NN) = (n_1/N)(n_2/N)$ or $P(E_1 \,\&\, E_2) = P(E_1)P(E_2)$. This result is Eq. 5.5 for the two basic experiments case.

Following exactly the same procedure for $3, 4, \ldots, m$ basic experiments, the reader can now easily obtain Eq. 5.5 exactly.[3] Eq. 5.5 can also be readily obtained for subjective basic experiments by following this same procedure, and interpreting $n_1, n_2, n_{1,2}$, etc., as the occurrences that would be expected to occur if the compound experiment were performed N times.

Now that we have developed formulas for two-category permutations, for the addition theorem for mutually exclusive events, and for the multiplication theorem for independent events, we can derive the binomial probability distribution.

---

[3] For example, in the three basic experiments case, $P(E_3 \mid E_1 \,\&\, E_2) = n_{1,2,3}/n_{1,2}$ would denote the probability that E_3 occurred given that E_1 and E_2 have occurred. Because of independence, $P(E_3 \mid E_1 \,\&\, E_2) = P(E_3) = n_3/N$. Hence, $n_{1,2,3}/N = (n_{1,2}/N)(n_3/N) = (n_1/N)(n_2/N)(n_3/N)$.

5.5   BINOMIAL PROBABILITY DISTRIBUTION

A binomial experiment is a stochastic compound experiment which has the following characteristics:

(a) The basic experiments making up the compound
experiment are identical.
(b) All possible outcomes in a basic experiment can
be placed into exactly one of two possible categories. Each category is called a fundamental
event for the basic experiment. Thus each basic
experiment can generate either one of two fundamental events.
(c) Since all the basic experiments in the compound
experiment are identical, the probability of any
one of the two possible fundamental events occurring is the same for all basic experiments.
(d) The basic experiments, and therefore the fundamental events, are independent.

5.51   Two Examples.   To illustrate a binomial experiment, assume we have a box containing 2 white and 3 green golf balls.
A compound experiment consists of four identical basic experiments. In each basic experiment a ball is drawn from the box,
its color is recorded, and then it is returned to the box. There
are five possible outcomes in each basic experiment, each of
which can be placed in one of two categories. The two fundamental events are "a white ball" (denoted by E) and "a green
ball" (denoted by F). On each basic experiment, $P(E) = .4$
and $P(F) = .6$. Since the probability of each fundamental event
is not affected by the outcome of any other basic experiment,
these events are independent.

As a second example, assume it is known that forty percent of the 1,000 housewives in City A answered "Yes" to a
particular question. A compound experiment consists of two
identical basic experiments. In each basic experiment a housewife is selected at random and asked the same question. There
are 1,000 possible outcomes in the first basic experiment and,
once this housewife has been chosen, 999 possible outcomes in
the second basic experiment. Each outcome can be placed in

one of two categories. The two fundamental events are "Yes" (denoted by $\underline{Y}$) and "No" (denoted by $\underline{N}$). Strickly speaking, the probability of a fundamental event on the second basic experiment is affected by the outcome of the first basic experiment. For example, if $\underline{Y}$ occurred on the first basic experiment, $\underline{P}(\underline{Y})$ on the second basic experiment is 399/999, while if $\underline{N}$ occurred on the first basic experiment, $\underline{P}(\underline{Y})$ on the second basic experiment is 400/999. Moreover, $\underline{P}(\underline{Y})$ on the first experiment is 400/1,000. Thus, strictly speaking, the independence and constant probability conditions for binomial experiments are violated. However, since the sample size (2) is small relative to the population size (1,000), $\underline{P}(\underline{Y})$ is not noticeably different from .400 on any basic experiment. Hence, for practical purposes, we can interpret this as a binomial experiment.

5.52   Binomial Random Variable and Probability Distribution.

Let $\underline{E}$ and $\underline{F}$ denote the two possible fundamental events in a basic experiment. We shall call the series of fundamental events observed, when a binomial experiment is performed, a compound fundamental event. A binomial random variable, denoted by $\underline{B}$, is defined as a relationship between the set of possible compound fundamental events and a set of numbers (the values of $\underline{B}$) which indicates the number of times $\underline{E}$ occurred in the corresponding compound fundamental event.

To illustrate these concepts, take the box example described at the beginning of the preceding section. Table 5.1 shows this random variable. All possible compound fundamental events are listed in the first column. Note for example, that the compound fundamental event $\underline{EEFF}$ denotes "$\underline{E}$ occurred on the first two basic experiments and $\underline{F}$ on the third and fourth basic experiments". The remaining notation is consistent with that introduced in previous chapters. Notice that the values of $\underline{B}$ can range from 0 to the number of basic experiments in the binomial experiment (in this case, 4).

Table 5.2 shows the probability distribution for $\underline{B}$. We shall now derive a formula for obtaining these binomial probabilities.

In Table 5.1, we note, for example, that the fundamental event $\underline{E}$ occurs once ($\underline{b}$ = 1) if any one of 4 mutually exclusive compound fundamental events occur. Each of these compound fundamental events contains 1 $\underline{E}$ and 3 $\underline{F}$'s. Since the fundamental events making up each compound fundamental event are

TABLE 5.1

BINOMIAL RANDOM VARIABLE $\underline{B}$
FOR BOX EXAMPLE

$\underline{x}$	$\underline{B}(\underline{x})$
FFFF	0
EFFF	1
FEFF	1
FFEF	1
FFFE	1
EEFF	2
EFEF	2
EFFE	2
FFEE	2
FEFE	2
FEEF	2
EEEF	3
EEFE	3
EFEE	3
FEEE	3
EEEE	4

TABLE 5.2

PROBABILITY DISTRIBUTION FOR $\underline{B}$

Value of $\underline{B}$ $\underline{b}$	$\underline{P}(\underline{b})$
0	.1296
1	.3456
2	.3456
3	.1536
4	.0256
	1.0000

independent, the probability of each of these compound funda-
mental events is (from Eq. 5.5) $[\underline{P}(\underline{E})]^1 [\underline{P}(\underline{F})]^3 = .4^1(.6^3) =$
.0864. Since $\underline{b} = 1$ occurs if any one of these 4 mutually ex-
clusive compound fundamental events occurs, we can use Eq.
5.4 to obtain $\underline{P}(\underline{b} = 1) = .0864 + .0864 + .0864 + .0864 =$
$4(.0864) = .3456$. The second row of Table 5.2 shows this.
Note that the number of compound fundamental events yielding just one $\underline{E}$ corresponds exactly to the number of two-category permutations where $\underline{s} = 1$ and $\underline{n} = 4$ (see Eq. 5.3).

Similarly, the number of compound fundamental events in
which $\underline{E}$ occurs twice is seen (Table 5.1) to be the number of
two-category permutations where $\underline{s} = 2$ and $\underline{n} = 4$. The prob-
ability of each event is $[\underline{P}(\underline{E})]^2 [\underline{P}(\underline{F})]^2$ and therefore $\underline{P}(\underline{b} = 2) =$
$[4!/(2!2!)](.4^2)(.6^2) = .3456$ (see Table 5.2).

The reader should now be able to put together the pieces
for the general case. If a binomial experiment containing $\underline{n}$
basic experiments is performed, the probability, denoted by
$\underline{B}[\underline{s} \mid \underline{n}, \underline{P}(\underline{E})]$, of a compound fundamental event in which the
fundamental event $\underline{E}$ occurs $\underline{b} = \underline{s}$ times (i.e., the probability
of a value of $\underline{s}$ for the binomial random variable) is given by
the following binomial probability formula:

$$\underline{B}[\underline{s} \mid \underline{n}, \underline{P}(\underline{E})] = \frac{n!}{s!(n-s)!} \, \underline{P}(\underline{E})^{\underline{s}} [1 - \underline{P}(\underline{E})]^{\underline{n}-\underline{s}} \qquad (5.6)$$

The symbol $\underline{B}[\underline{s} \mid \underline{n}, \underline{P}(\underline{E})]$ is read "the probability of event $\underline{E}$
occurring $\underline{s}$ times given that $\underline{n}$ basic experiments are per-
formed and given the probability $\underline{P}(\underline{E})$ that $\underline{E}$ will occur on any
one basic experiment". The quantity $\underline{n}!/[\underline{s}!(\underline{n}-\underline{s})!]$ (Eq. 5.3
indicates the number of mutually exclusive compound funda-
mental events containing $\underline{s}$ $\underline{E}$'s (and $\underline{n}-\underline{s}$ $\underline{F}$'s), and the quantity
$\underline{P}(\underline{E})^{\underline{s}}[1 - \underline{P}(\underline{E})]^{\underline{n}-\underline{s}}$ indicates the identical probability of each
of these compound events.[4] The reader should use Eq. 5.6 to
check the remaining probabilities given in Table 5.2 .

---

[4] In practice, the tedious calculation of Eq. 5.6 is avoided by using published tables.
For example, see Table of the Cumulative Binomial Probabilities, Ordnance Corps
Pamphlet ORDP 20-1, 1952 (which gives binomial distribution to 7 decimal places for
all values of $\underline{n}$ up to 150 and $\underline{P}(\underline{E})$ in intervals of .01); and Tables of the Cumulative
Binomial Probability Distribution, Harvard University Press, 1955 (gives values of $\underline{P}(\underline{E})$
to 5 decimal places in intervals of .01 for various values of $\underline{n}$ up to 1,000).

As another example, assume that a manufacturing process turns out defective parts at random. If the process is working correctly, twenty percent of the parts produced will be defective. To protect itself against a faulty process which is turning out more than twenty percent defectives, the firm decides to take samples of five parts at stated intervals of time. If at any time 4 or more parts are defective, the process will be checked over. What is the probability that the process will be needlessly checked?

We can treat this sample as a binomial experiment containing 5 identical basic experiments, each of which is the selection of a part from the assembly line. The occurrence of a defective part is a fundamental event which we denote by $\underline{E}$. We are interested in the probability of obtaining a compound fundamental event containing 4 or 5 $\underline{E}$'s when $\underline{P}(\underline{E}) = .2$. From Eq. 5.6 we have

$$\underline{B}(4 \mid 5, .2) = [5!/(4!1!)].2^4(.8)^1 = .00640$$

$$\underline{B}(5 \mid 5, .2) = [5!/(5!0!)].2^5(.8)^0 = .00032$$

Thus the probability of needlessly checking the process is .00640 + .00032 = .00672.

The Exercise section at the end of this chapter, as well as the next section and the remaining chapters, will treat some of the many important applications of the binomial probability distribution.

5.6   BAYES' THEOREM AND A MACHINE SET-UP APPLICATION

In this section, we shall derive the multiplication theorem for dependent events. Next, we shall use this theorem to develop Bayes' Theorem. Finally, we shall utilize Bayes' Theorem and the binomial probability distribution to solve a machine set-up problem.

5.61   Dependent Events.   In a compound experiment, if the probability of any given basic event occurring on any given basic experiment is affected by the outcomes of the preceding basic experiments, we say the basic experiments and the basic events are dependent. For example, assume we have 2 identical boxes. Box 1 contains 3 white and 3 black golf balls, and Box 2 contains 2 white, 4 black, and 4 green golf balls. A compound experiment consists of two basic experiments. The first basic experiment involves selecting one of the boxes at random. The second basic experiment consists of drawing a ball from the box selected in the first experiment. The probability of, say, the event "a white ball" in the second basic experiment is dependent on the outcome of the first experiment. If Box 1 is selected, the probability of "a white ball" on the second experiment is $3/6 = .5$. But if Box 2 is selected, the probability of "a white ball" on the second experiment is $2/10 = .20$. Since the probability of the event "a white ball" on the second experiment depends on the outcome of the first experiment, the two basic events in this compound experiment are dependent.

In this book, when we deal with dependent basic experiments we shall only consider compound experiments containing two dependent basic experiments. Hence, the derivations which follow will only treat this case explicitly. However, the procedures for derivations involving m (m > 2) dependent basic experiments are identical. Hence, the reader should be able to readily obtain these derivations if he follows closely the procedure given for the two experiments case.

5.62 Multiplication Theorem for the Two Dependent Basic Experiments Case.

Let two basic a priori experiments be performed. Assume these experiments are dependent. Let $\underline{E}_1$ denote a basic event defined for the first experiment and $\underline{E}_2$ a basic event defined for the second experiment. We wish to determine the probability of the the compound event $\underline{E}_1 \underline{E}_2$; i.e., we wish to determine the probability that event $\underline{E}_1$ will occur on the first experiment and $\underline{E}_2$ on the second. We denote this probability by $\underline{P}(\underline{E}_1 \& \underline{E}_2)$, as before.

Let $\underline{N}_1$ denote the number of possible outcomes in the first basic experiment, and let $\underline{N}_2|_1$ denote the number of outcomes possible in the second basic experiment given that $\underline{E}_1$ occurred in the first experiment. Let $\underline{n}_1$ denote the number of outcomes in the first experiment contained in $\underline{E}_1$ and $\underline{n}_2|_1$ the number of outcomes in the second experiment contained in $\underline{E}_2$ given that $\underline{E}_1$ occurred. The total number of possible compound outcomes is $\underline{N}_1(\underline{N}_2|_1)$. Of these outcomes, $\underline{n}_1(\underline{n}_2|_1)$ correspond to the compound event $E_1 E_2$. Since these compound outcomes are equally likely, we have

$$P(E_1 \& E_2) = (n_1 n_2 \mid_1) / (N_1 N_2 \mid_1) = (n_1 / N_1)(n_2 \mid_1 / N_2 \mid_1)$$
$$= P(E_1)P(E_2 \mid E_1) \qquad (5.7)$$

where, as before, $P(E_2 \mid E_1)$ denotes the <u>conditional</u> probability of E_2 occurring given that E_1 has occurred. Eq. 5.7 is known as the multiplication theorem for two dependent events.

As an example, assume that five boxes are mixed up. These boxes are identical except for color and contents. Two boxes are green and three are red. Each of the green boxes contains 3 white and 3 black golf balls, and each of the red boxes contains 2 white, 4 black, and 4 blue golf balls. A compound experiment consists of selecting a box at random (the first basic experiment) and then drawing a ball from this box (the second basic experiment). Let E_1 denote the event "a green box" and E_2 the event "a white ball". Find $P(E_1 \& E_2)$.

We have $P(E_1) = n_1 / N_1 = 2/5 = .4$ and $P(E_2 \mid E_1) = n_2 \mid_1 / N_2 \mid_1 = 3/6 = .5$. Hence, from Eq. 5.7, $P(E_1 \& E_2) = P(E_1)P(E_2 \mid E_1) = .4(.5) = .2$.

If E_1 denotes the event "a red box" and E_2 the event "a white ball", what is $P(E_1 \& E_2)$? In this case we have $P(E_1) = n_1 / N_1 = 3/5 = .6$ and $P(E_2 \mid E_1) = n_2 \mid_1 / N_2 \mid_1 = 2/10 = .2$. Thus $P(E_1 \& E_2) = .6(.2) = .12$.

Eq. 5.7 was derived with respect to a priori experiments. Exactly the same result holds for empirical and subjective experiments. To illustrate, assume a compound experiment is performed a great many, say N, times. Two dependent basic empirical experiments make up this compound experiment. Let n_1 denote the number of times event E_1 occurred in the first experiment, and $n_2 \mid_1$ the number of times E_2 occurred in the second experiment <u>when</u> E_1 has also occurred in the first experiment. We know that $P(E_2 \mid E_1) = n_2 \mid_1 / n_1$. Dividing the numerator and denominator of the right-hand side of this expression by N yields $P(E_2 \mid E_1) = (n_2 \mid_1 / N)/(n_1 / N)$. By cross multiplying we obtain $n_2 \mid_1 / N = (n_1 / N)P(E_2 \mid E_1)$ or $P(E_1 \& E_2) = P(E_1)P(E_2 \mid E_1)$, which coincides with Eq. 5.7. The same procedure yields the same result for subjective experiments if we assume that n_1 and $n_2 \mid_1$ are the expected occurrences if the compound experiment were performed N times.

5.63 Prior and Posterior Probabilities. Assume a compound experiment composed of two dependent basic events is performed.

Assume, further, that prior to the performance of the first basic experiment, we know the probabilities of the simple events possible in the first basic experiment. These probabilities are called _prior_ probabilities. Assume, finally, that we know which event occurred on the second basic experiment.

Bayes' theorem enables us to use this information concerning the observed event of the second basic experiment to revise the probabilities of the possible simple events in the first experiment. These revised prior probabilities are called _poster-ior_ or Bayes' probabilities.

This terminology will become clearer as we proceed.

5.64 Bayes' Theorem. Assume that the first basic experiment described in the preceding section can generate any one of m simple events. Let these possible events be denoted by E_1, $E_2, \ldots, E_m$. The probability of E_i ($i = 1, 2, \ldots, m$) occurring on the first basic experiment, if this were the only experiment performed, is denoted by $P(E_i)$. Thus the $P(E_i)$ ($i = 1, 2, \ldots m$) are the prior probabilities for the first basic experiment.

Now, assume the compound experiment is performed, and we are told that the basic event F occurred on the second basic experiment. Given this information, what is the probability that the event E_i (where i is any number $1, 2, \ldots, m$) occurred on the first experiment? We know that prior to the performance of the compound experiment, the probability of E_i is $P(E_i)$; but now we want to know how the occurrence of the event F affects this prior probability. That is, we seek the revised or posterior probability of E_i. This posterior probability is denoted by $P(E_i \mid F)$ (read "the probability of E_i on the first experiment given that F occurred on the second experiment").

We proceed by first determining the probability that event F will occur on the second basic experiment. Event F will occur on the second basic experiment if any one of m mutually exclusive compound events occur. These compound events are $E_1 F$, $E_2 F, \ldots,$ and $E_m F$. Since E_i and F are dependent events, the probability of any compound event $E_i F$ can be determined from Eq. 5.7. That is, $P(E_i \& F) = P(E_i) P(F \mid E_i)$. From Eq.

5.4, we thus determine the probability of $\underline{F}$ occurring on the second experiment:

$$\underline{P}(\underline{F}) = \underline{P}(\underline{E}_1)\underline{P}(\underline{F} \mid \underline{E}_1) + \underline{P}(\underline{E}_2)\underline{P}(\underline{F} \mid \underline{E}_2) + \ldots$$
$$+ \underline{P}(\underline{E}_m)\underline{P}(\underline{F} \mid \underline{E}_m) \qquad (5.8)$$

Now, if this compound experiment is performed many, say $\underline{N}$, times, the basic event $\underline{F}$ on the second experiment will occur $\underline{n}_1 = \underline{P}(\underline{F})(\underline{N})$ times. Moreover, the compound event $\underline{E}_i\underline{F}$ will occur $\underline{n}_i = \underline{P}(\underline{E}_i)\underline{P}(\underline{F} \mid \underline{E}_i)(\underline{N})$ times. From Definition 2.2, the probability of $\underline{E}_i$ having occurred on the first experiment given that $\underline{F}$ has occurred on the second experiment is therefore $\underline{P}(\underline{E}_i \mid \underline{F}) = \underline{n}_i / \underline{n}_1 = [\underline{P}(\underline{E}_i)\underline{P}(\underline{F} \mid \underline{E}_i)] / \underline{P}(\underline{F})$. Substituting Eq. 5.8 into this expression yields Bayes' theorem:

$$\underline{P}(\underline{E}_i \mid \underline{F}) = [\underline{P}(\underline{E}_i)\underline{P}(\underline{F} \mid \underline{E}_i)] / [\underline{P}(\underline{E}_1)\underline{P}(\underline{F} \mid \underline{E}_1)$$
$$+ \underline{P}(\underline{E}_2)\underline{P}(\underline{F} \mid \underline{E}_2) + \ldots + \underline{P}(\underline{E}_m)\underline{P}(\underline{F} \mid \underline{E}_m)] \quad (5.9)$$

To take a familiar example, assume we have two green and three red boxes. Each green box contains 3 white and 3 black golf balls, and each red box contains 2 white, 4 black, and 4 blue golf balls. As the first basic experiment, one of the boxes is selected at random. $\underline{m} = 2$ simple events are possible: "a green box" (denoted by $\underline{E}_1$) and "a red box" (denoted by $\underline{E}_2$). The prior probabilities are $\underline{P}(\underline{E}_1) = 2/5 = .4$ and $\underline{P}(\underline{E}_2) = 3/5 = .6$. The second basic experiment involves drawing a ball from the box selected on the first experiment. Assume the event (denoted by $\underline{F}$) which occurs is "a white ball". The conditional probabilities are $\underline{P}(\underline{F} \mid \underline{E}_1) = 3/6 = .5$ and $\underline{P}(\underline{F} \mid \underline{E}_2) = 2/10 = .2$. What is the probability, given this information, that the box selected was green, i.e., that $\underline{E}_1$ occurred on the first basic experiment?

Before the results of the second basic experiment were known, the probability of selecting a green box was $\underline{P}(\underline{E}_1) = .4$. Using Bayes' theorem, we can revise this prior probability in light of the additional information. We find that the probability that a green box was selected is now

$$\underline{P}(\underline{E}_1 \mid \underline{F}) = [\underline{P}(\underline{E}_1)\underline{P}(\underline{F} \mid \underline{E}_1)] / [\underline{P}(\underline{E}_1)\underline{P}(\underline{F} \mid \underline{E}_1) + \underline{P}(\underline{E}_2)\underline{P}(\underline{F} \mid \underline{E}_2)] =$$
$$.4(.5) / [.4(.5) + .6(.2)] = .625.$$

Suppose $\underline{G}$ denotes the event "a blue ball". What is $P(E_1 \mid G)$? Since $P(G \mid E_1) = 0$ and $P(G \mid E_2) = .4$, we have $P(E_1 \mid G) = [.4(0)] / [.4(0) + .6(.4)] = 0$. The reader should calculate $P(E_2 \mid F)$ and $P(E_2 \mid G)$ and compare these probabilities with $P(E_2)$. He should also calculate $P(E_1 \mid H)$ and $P(E_2 \mid H)$ (where H denotes the event "a black ball") and compare these posterior probabilities with their corresponding prior probabilities.

5.65 Machine Set-up Application.

A metal working manufacturer receives an order for 1,000 special purpose gears. Two alternative procedures are available for setting the tolerances on the machines required to produce the gears. First, a team of ordinary and apprentice mechanics can be used and no checkup made on their work. Past experience shows that, in this case, the machines will have a defective rate of d_1 = .05 about fifty percent of the time, a defective rate of d_2 = .10 about forty percent of the time, and a defective rate of d_3 = .30 about ten percent of the time. Thus, $P(d_1)$ = .5, $P(d_2)$ = .4, and $P(d_3)$ = .1. As a second alternative, a team of master mechanics can be called in to check the tolerances after they have been set by the ordinary and apprentice mechanics. In this case, the machines are certain to have a defective rate of .05.

The material and labor cost for producing the lot of 1,000 gears is $50,000 if ordinary and apprentice mechanics alone are used, and $51,000 if the master mechanics are also brought in. Each defective gear produced in this lot of 1,000 gears can be made acceptable by a special hand-finishing operation. But the cost of this operation is $10 per gear.

Assume that the production of 1,000 gears can be viewed as part of an endless stream of production in which the occurrence of defective gears meets the conditions of a compound binomial experiment. If the information given so far is the only available information, should the master mechanics be called in?

If the master mechanics are used, we expect 1,000(.05) = 50 defective gears to be produced, so that the expected refinishing cost in this case is 50($10) = $500. Adding the material and labor cost when the master mechanics are used yields an expected cost of $500 + $51,000 = $51,500 for the job.

If only the ordinary and apprentice mechanics are used, the refinishing cost will be either [1,000(.05)]($10) = $500, [1,000(.10)]($10) = $1,000, or [1,000(.30)]($10) = $3,000, depending on the actual defective rate. Thus the cost for the job will be either $50,000 + $500 = $50,500, $50,000 + $1,000 = $51,000, or $50,000 + $3,000 = $53,000.

These costs are values of a random variable $\underline{C}^A$ "job cost without master mechanics". They are related to the outcomes of the experiment performed when the machines are set up. Table 5.3 shows this random variable and its probability distribution and expected value. The notation used is consistent with that developed in preceding chapters. We see that $\underline{E}(\underline{C}^A) =$ $50,950 is less than the expected cost of $51,500 associated with the master mechanics. Thus if the firm were to make its decision at this point, it would not use the team of master mechanics to check the work of the ordinary and apprentice mechanics.

TABLE 5.3

RANDOM VARIABLE $\underline{C}^A$ AND ITS PROBABILITY
DISTRIBUTION AND EXPECTED VALUE

Outcome of Experiment $\underline{d}$	$\underline{C}^A(\underline{d}) = \underline{c}^A$	$\underline{P}(\underline{c}^A)$	$\underline{E}(\underline{C}^A)$
.05	50,500	.5	25,250
.10	51,000	.4	20,400
.30	53,000	.1	5,300
		1.0	50,950

Now assume that the ordinary and apprentice mechanics have set up the machines. Before deciding whether to call in the master mechanics, a sample of 10 gears is produced and inspected. Five gears are found to be defective. Given this additional information, should the master mechanics be called in?

To answer this question, we must determine the posterior probabilities of the simple events of the first basic experiment. That is, before the results of this sample were available, we had $\underline{P}(\underline{d}_1) = .5$, $\underline{P}(\underline{d}_2) = .4$, and $\underline{P}(\underline{d}_3) = .1$; now that we know the machines have produced 5 defectives out of a sample of 10 gears, we can revise these prior probabilities. For example, it would seem, intuitively, that this sample result is more consistent with $\underline{d}_3$ than with $\underline{d}_1$. Let $\underline{k}$ denote this sample result of

$\underline{s}$ = 5 defectives in a sample of $\underline{n}$ = 10 gears. Then we can use Eq. 5.9 to calculate the posterior probabilities $\underline{P}(\underline{d_1} \mid \underline{k})$, $\underline{P}(\underline{d_2} \mid \underline{k})$, and $\underline{P}(\underline{d_3} \mid \underline{k})$. The expected value of the random variable $\underline{C}^R$ "job cost without master mechanics based on sample information" can be determined using these probabilities.

From Eq. 5.6 we have $\underline{P}(\underline{k} \mid \underline{d_1}) = \underline{B}(5 \mid 10, .05) = .0001$, $\underline{P}(\underline{k} \mid \underline{d_2}) = \underline{B}(5 \mid 10, .10) = .0015$, and $\underline{P}(\underline{k} \mid \underline{d_3}) = \underline{B}(5 \mid 10, .30) = .1030$. From Eq. 5.9 we have $\underline{P}(\underline{d_i} \mid \underline{k}) = [\underline{P}(\underline{d_i})\underline{P}(\underline{k} \mid \underline{d_i})]$ / $[\underline{P}(\underline{d_1})\underline{P}(\underline{k} \mid \underline{d_1}) + \underline{P}(\underline{d_2})\underline{P}(\underline{k} \mid \underline{d_2}) + \underline{P}(\underline{d_3})\underline{P}(\underline{k} \mid \underline{d_3})]$ so that

$$\underline{P}(\underline{d_1} \mid \underline{k}) = [.5(.0001)] / [.5(.0001)+.4(.0015)+.1(.1030)]=.0046$$
$$\underline{P}(\underline{d_2} \mid \underline{k}) = [.4(.0015)] / [.5(.0001)+.4(.0015)+.1(.1030)]=.0548$$
$$\underline{P}(\underline{d_3} \mid \underline{k}) = [.1(.1030)] / [.5(.0001)+.4(.0015)+.1(.1030)]=.9406$$

We see that the sample result has drastically changed the probability that the machines have a defective rate of .05. Before the sample is taken, this probability is .5; after the sample is taken, it falls to .0046. Similarly, the probability that the defective rate is .3 has changed dramatically from .1 to .9406.

Table 5.4 shows that, as a result of revising the prior probabilities in the light of sample information, the expected cost of letting the machine set-up go unchecked is $52,879. Thus, since it would cost only $51,500 to call in the master mechanics, the best decision now is to call in the master mechanics.[5]

---

[5] For a detailed discussion of other aspects of this application, e.g., the optimum sample size, the reader is referred to S. Goldberg, Probability, Englewood Cliffs: Prentice-Hall, 1960, pp. 286-292; J. Kemeny, A. Schleifer, J. Snell, G. Thompson, Finite Mathematics with Business Applications, Englewood Cliffs: Prentice-Hall, Inc., 1962, pp. 221-5; and R. Schlaifer, Probability, and Statistics for Business Decisions, New York: McGraw-Hill Book Co., 1959.

TABLE 5.4

RANDOM VARIABLE $\underline{C}^R$ AND ITS PROBABILITY DISTRIBUTION AND EXPECTED VALUE

$\underline{d}$	$\underline{C}^R(\underline{d}) = \underline{c}^R$	$\underline{P}(\underline{c}^R)$	$\underline{E}(\underline{C}^R)$
.05	50,500	.0046	232
.10	51,000	.0548	2,795
.30	53,000	.9406	49,852
			52,879

5.7 DISCUSSION AND REVIEW QUESTIONS

1. Distinguish between ordinary and two-category permutations.

2. Distinguish between the addition theorem for mutually exclusive events, the multiplication theorems for independent and dependent events, and Bayes' theorem.

3. Distinguish between compound, basic, and fundamental events.

4. What are the characteristics of binomial experiments?

5. How are two-category permutations, the addition theorem for mutually exclusive events, and the multiplication theorem for independent events used to derive the binomial probability distribution?

6. Distinguish between prior and posterior probabilities.

5.8 EXERCISES

1. If a manufacturing process is working correctly, 10 percent of the items turned out will be defective. A sample of 8 items is taken. Assuming that the binomial probability distribution is applicable:

      (a) What is the probability of 5 items being defective if the process is working correctly? (Ans.: .0004)

(b) If you were a quality control inspector, would you take any action, given that 5 items are found defective?

2. A company has a forty percent dropout rate in its training program. What is the probability that the company will get 7 or more dropouts from its current training group of 10 persons? (Ans.: .0548)

3. A truck fleet has a trip accident probability of .02. What is the probability that no truck will have an accident if 2 trucks are sent out? if 4 trucks are sent out?

4. From past experience it is known that thirty percent of the items started in a manufacturing process will turn out defective. We want to have at least a .9 probability of ending up with at least 4 good items. How many items should we start, i.e., what is the minimum scrap allowance ? (Hint: Set $\underline{n}$ = 7 and compute the probability of 4 or more good items; then set $\underline{n}$ = 8 and compute this same probability).

5. In the machine set-up application in Section 5.6, what is the best decision if:

(a) 1 defective gear is found in the sample of 10?
(b) 5 defective gears in a sample of 20 are found?

6. A lot containing 1,000 parts is received from a supplier. In the past, sixty percent of all such lots have had ten percent defective parts, thirty percent have had twenty percent defective parts, and ten percent have had fifty percent defective parts. Five parts are selected at random from this lot, and 1 defective part is found. Before the sample was selected, what was the probability of receiving a lot that was twenty percent defective? Given the sample result, what is the probability that the box originally contained twenty percent defective parts?

7. It is known, from past surveys, that in forty percent of the families in Town A the head of the family will not be at home on a typical weekday evening. A personal interviewer from the market research department of a firm is assigned six families at random; he is to call, unannounced, on each family and interview the head of the family. On a typical weekday evening, what is the probability that:

(a) he will find no heads of families at home? (Ans.: .0467)
(b) he will find all six heads of families at home? (Ans.: .0041)

(c) he will find at least one head of the family at
   home? (Ans.: .9533)

8. A firm, which introduced a new consumer product by
advertising in a nationally circulated magazine, now wishes
to measure the effectiveness of this promotional strategy.
From sales records, the firm knows that five percent of the
potential customers have purchased the product since the advertisement. A national survey shows that forty percent of
the potential customers saw the advertisement. A survey of
purchases at the point of purchase indicates that ninety percent of the purchasers saw the advertisement.

(a) What is the probability that a potential customer
   bought the product and also saw the advertisement? (Ans.: .045)
(b) What is the probability that a potential customer
   who saw the advertisement bought the product?
   [Ans.: .1125; note that $\underline{P}(\underline{E}_1 \& \underline{E}_2) = \underline{P}(\underline{E}_2 \& \underline{E}_1)$
   and, from Eq. 5.7, $\underline{P}(\underline{E}_2 \mid \underline{E}_1) = \underline{P}(\underline{E}_1 \& \underline{E}_2)/(\underline{P}(\underline{E}_1))$].

9. The performance of an experienced stock market an-
alyst is being studied. Let $\underline{E}_1$ denote the event "the analyst
predicts that the Dow-Jones Industrial Average will not fall
tomorrow", $\underline{E}_2$ the event "the analyst predicts that the Dow-
Jones Industrial Average will fall tomorrow", $\underline{F}_1$ the event
"the Dow-Jones Industrial Average does not fall tomorrow",
and $\underline{F}_2$ the event "the Dow-Jones Industrial Average falls tomorrow". From past records we determine that $\underline{P}(\underline{E}_1 \mid \underline{F}_1) =$
.7 and $(\underline{P}(\underline{E}_2 \mid \underline{F}_2) = .8$. We also know that in the current
type of bull market, the Dow-Jones Industrial Average does
not fall about ninety percent of the time.

(a) If the analyst predicts that the Average will not
   fall tomorrow, what is the posterior probability
   that it will not fall tomorrow? (Ans.: .97)
(b) If the analyst predicts that the Average will fall
   tomorrow, what is the posterior probability
   that it will fall tomorrow? (Ans.: .23)
(c) If the analyst predicts that the Average will fall
   tomorrow, what is the Bayes probability that it
   will not fall tomorrow?

10. A firm is considering the introduction of a new product.
The market research department of the firm feels that there is

a .6 probability that the product will be successful. If successful, the product will generate $100,000 of profit over its life-
time. If unsuccessful, the product will result in a loss of
$200,000.

  (a) Should the firm introduce the new product?
  (b) The firm decides to market test the product in
      several test cities before making a final decision.
      It finds that, if the product is going to be success-
      ful, the test results observed will occur with prob-
      ability .8; if the product is going to be unsuccess-
      ful, the test results observed will occur with prob-
      ability .1 .
      (1) What are the prior and posterior probabilities
          of a successfully and unsuccessfully marketed
          product? (Ans.: posterior probabilities are
          .92 and .08, respectively)
      (2) On the basis of the market test results, should
          the firm introduce the new product?

6 ▶   PROBABILITY MODELS FOR SCRAP
ALLOWANCE AND QUEUING PROBLEMS

6.1 MOTIVATION

In this chapter we shall show how probability analysis can be used to solve scrap allowance and queuing problems. The scrap allowance model, another type of expected value model, is based on the binomial probability distribution. The queuing model utilizes expected value to treat a particular feature of the model, but is essentially developed on the basis of Eqs. 5.4 and 5.5. This latter model also serves as an introduction to a class of problems which is of considerable importance in the field of operations research.

6.2 SCRAP ALLOWANCE MODEL

A manufacturer produces special purpose parts and equipment to order. Each order is different and typically is never repeated. An order comes in for 15 parts. These parts require machining, furnace, molding, and assembly operations, in that order. It is expected that it will take one week to complete this order. The first operation, machining, takes only a few hours. However, it is a very expensive operation, the cost for machine set-up (measured in terms of the mechanic's labor and the scrap material utilized to set tolerances) being $300 regardless of the number of parts actually started (initially machined). Furthermore, since other demands are continually being placed on these machines, they cannot be kept idle for a whole week until the current job is completed; rather, they must be immediately reset for the next job.

On the basis of past experience, the firm knows that 5 percent of the parts started in this type of process will turn out defective by the end of the entire manufacturing process. These defective parts are produced at random. Moreover, the entire operation can be viewed as a continuous stream of production over time, the special order for 15 parts being just a minor segment of this stream. Hence, the probability of obtaining 0,1,2,... defective parts in a production run of 15,16... parts is given by the binomial probability distribution.

It is evident that if the firm starts exactly 15, or even more, parts, it may well end up with less than 15 nondefective parts. Since the firm guarantees that all parts shipped will be nondefective, if less than 15 parts are successfully completed in a production lot of 15,16,... parts, the machines must be set up all over again at the fixed cost of $300. In order to ensure that none of the parts produced in the second run are defective, the firm checks each of these parts at every stage in the manufacturing process. While this procedure guarantees that no more than two machine set-ups will ever be required to fill out any order, it results in a doubling of the material and labor costs of each part produced in the second lot. Since the material and labor costs incurred in normal production (the first run) total $50 per part, they increase to $100 per part in the second production run.

The firm can minimize the probability of ever incurring the high cost associated with a second run by producing more parts, in the first run, than it actually requires to fill out the order. The greater the amount by which actual production exceeds the quantity ordered, the smaller is the probability of incurring the expense of a second run. However, each order represents special purpose parts which will typically never be re-ordered. This means that nondefective parts produced in excess of the specified quantity ordered will never be sold, and, since their salvage value is negligible, they represent a total loss.

Thus each time an order comes in, the firm must decide how many parts it should start in order to minimize the total cost of production on the average in the long run. That is, it must determine the optimum scrap allowance. This decision must balance two contrasting cost patterns. That is, it must take note of the fact that as the number of parts started increases, the cost associated with excess production increases, but the cost associated with second set-up production decreases.

6.21   An Expected Value Solution.

6.21   An Expected Value Solution.   If the firm decides to start N parts ($N \geq 15$), what is the expected cost of 15 nondefective parts? We can think of the machining of N parts as a binomial experiment. The values of the corresponding binomial random variable B are the possible numbers of defective parts. Denoting these values by b, we have $b = 0, 1, 2, \ldots, N$. Let C^N denote another random variable "machining cost for 15 nondefective parts when N parts are started" whose value [denoted by $C^N(b)$] is the cost incurred when the value b occurs, N units are started, and 15 nondefective parts are produced.

We can find the values $C^N(b)$ from the following equations:

$$C^N(b) = 300 + 50N \qquad\qquad N-b \geq 15 \qquad (6.1)$$
$$C^N(b) = 600 + 50N + 100[15-(N-b)] \quad N-b < 15 \qquad (6.2)$$

Note that the quantity $N-b$ represents the number of nondefective parts produced in the first run.

To illustrate the use of Eqs. 6.1 and 6.2, assume that 17 parts are started, i.e., $N = 17$, and that 1 defective part occurs (b = 1) during the manufacturing process. Since $N-b = 17 - 1 = 16 > 15$, Eq. 6.1 is applicable. This equation is thus used when only one machine set-up is necessary. We find that the value $C^{17}(1)$ is the sum of: 1) the single machine set-up cost ($300) and 2) the cost of material and labor per part ($50) times the number of parts produced (17); i.e., $C^{17}(1) = 300 + 50(17) = 1,150$.

If $\underline{N}$ = 17 and $\underline{b}$ = 4, then, since $\underline{N}-\underline{b}$ = 17 - 4 = 13 < 15, Eq. 6.2 is applicable. This equation is therefore used when two machine set-ups are required. We find that the value of $\underline{C}^{17}(4)$ is the sum of: 1) two machine set-up costs ($300 + $300 = $600), 2) the cost of material and labor per part on the first run ($50) times the number of parts produced on the first run (17), and 3) the cost of material and labor per part on the second run ($100) times the number of parts produced on the second run (2); i.e., $\underline{C}^{17}(4)$ = 600 + 50(17) + 100(2) = 1,650.

The number of parts produced on the second set-up is given by 15-($\underline{N}-\underline{b}$) because $\underline{N}-\underline{b}$ represents the number of nondefective parts resulting from the first set-up, and, since Eq. 6.2 is only used when $\underline{N}-\underline{b}$ < 15, the difference 15-($\underline{N}-\underline{b}$) indicates how many additional parts must be produced to bring the total number of nondefective parts up to 15. For example, when $\underline{b}$ = 4 out of $\underline{N}$ = 17 parts are defective, $\underline{N}-\underline{b}$ = 17 - 4 = 13 parts are nondefective and, hence, 15-($\underline{N}-\underline{b}$) = 15 - 13 = 2 additional parts must be produced.

Table 6.1 shows the results of applying Eqs. 6.1 and 6.2 to determine values for $\underline{C}^{17}$ when $\underline{b}$ = 0,1,2,...,6 (why we have not computed $\underline{C}^{17}(\underline{b})$ for $\underline{b}$ > 6 will become evident shortly). If we let $\underline{c}^{17}$ denote the different possible values of $\underline{C}^{17}$ we have (from Table 6.1) $\underline{c}^{17}$ = 1,150, 1,550, 1,650, 1,750, 1,850,... Let $\underline{P}(\underline{c}^{17})$ denote the probability of $\underline{c}^{17}$. From Table 6.1, we see that the value $\underline{c}_1^{17}$ = 1,150 occurs if any one of the three simple events $\underline{b}$ = 0, $\underline{b}$ = 1, or $\underline{b}$ = 2 occurs. Since this is a binomial experiment, these probabilities are (using Eq. 5.6:

$$\underline{P}(\underline{b} = 0) = \underline{B}(0|17,.05) = .4181$$
$$\underline{P}(\underline{b} = 1) = \underline{B}(1|17,.05) = .3741$$
$$\underline{P}(\underline{b} = 2) = \underline{B}(2|17,.05) = \underline{.1575}$$
$$.9497$$

Hence, $\underline{P}(\underline{c}_1^{17})$ = $\underline{P}$(1,150) = .9497. In the same way, since $\underline{c}_2^{17}$ = 1,550, $\underline{c}_3^{17}$ = 1,650, $\underline{c}_4^{17}$ = 1,750, and $\underline{c}_5^{17}$ = 1,850 occur if the simple events $\underline{b}$ = 3, $\underline{b}$ = 4, $\underline{b}$ = 5, and $\underline{b}$ = 6 occur, respectively, we have

$$\underline{P}(\underline{c}_2^{17}) = \underline{P}(1,550) = \underline{P}(\underline{b} = 3) = \underline{B}(3|17,.05) = .0415$$
$$\underline{P}(\underline{c}_3^{17}) = \underline{P}(1,650) = \underline{P}(\underline{b} = 4) = \underline{B}(4|17,.05) = .0076$$
$$\underline{P}(\underline{c}_4^{17}) = \underline{P}(1,750) = \underline{P}(\underline{b} = 5) = \underline{B}(5|17,.05) = .0011$$
$$\underline{P}(\underline{c}_5^{17}) = \underline{P}(1,850) = \underline{P}(\underline{b} = 6) = \underline{B}(6|17,.05) = .0001$$

TABLE 6.1

RANDOM VARIABLE C^{17}

$\underline{b}$	$\underline{C}^{17}(\underline{b})$
0	1,150
1	1,150
2	1,150
3	1,550
4	1,650
5	1,750
6	1,850
.	.
.	.
.	.
17	.

Finally, since $\underline{P}(\underline{b}) = 0$ for $\underline{b} > 6$, $\underline{P}(\underline{c}_i^{17}) = 0$ for $\underline{i} > 5$.

Applying Eq. 3.1 , we find that the expected value of $\underline{C}^{17}$ [denoted by $\underline{E}(\underline{C}^{17})$] is

$$\underline{E}(\underline{C}^{17}) = \underline{c}_1^{17}\,\underline{P}(\underline{c}_1^{17}) + \ldots + \underline{c}_5^{17}\underline{P}(\underline{c}_5^{17}) + \underline{c}_6^{17}\underline{P}(\underline{c}_6^{17}) + \ldots$$

$$+ c_{17}^{17}\,\underline{P}(\underline{c}_{17}^{17}) = 1,150(.9497) + \ldots + 1,850\ (.0001)$$

$$+ \underline{c}_6^{17}(0) + \ldots + \underline{c}_{17}^{17}(0)$$

Note that all terms after the fifth term vanish, since they are multiplied by zero. Hence

$$\underline{E}(\underline{C}^{17}) = 1,150(.9497) + 1,550(.0415) + 1,650(.0076)$$
$$+ 1,750(.0011) + 1,850(.0001) = 1,171.$$

Thus the expected cost of machining 15 nondefective parts if $\underline{N} = 17$ parts are initially started is \$1,171. To determine the optimum $\underline{N}$, the firm should compute $\underline{E}(\underline{C}^N)$ for $\underline{N} = 15, 16, \ldots$ and select that $\underline{N}$ which corresponds to the minimum $\underline{E}(\underline{C}^N)$.

Note that all the $\underline{E}(\underline{C}^N)$ calculated are associated with random variables which are defined for different binomial experiments. For example $\underline{C}^{16}$ is a random variable defined for a binomial experiment composed of 16 basic experiments while $\underline{C}^{20}$ is defined for 20 basic experiments.

Table 6.2 shows the expected values for the random variables $\underline{C}^{15}, \ldots, \underline{C}^{20}$. Since $\underline{E}(\underline{C}^{17}) = 1,171$ is the minimum $\underline{E}(\underline{C}^{\underline{N}})$, we see that the best decision is to start 17 parts and produce 17 - 15 = 2 parts as a scrap allowance.

TABLE 6.2

EXPECTED VALUES $\underline{E}(\underline{C}^{15}), \ldots, \underline{E}(\underline{C}^{20})$

$\underline{N}$	$\underline{E}(\underline{C}^{\underline{N}})$
15	$1,286
16	1,182
17	1,171
18	1,205
19	1,251
20	1,300

6.22 General Formula. We shall now derive a general formula for problems of this sort. Let

$\underline{b}$	denote the number of defective parts produced in the first production run;
$\underline{N}$	denote the number of parts started;
$\underline{Z}$	denote the number of nondefective parts required;
$\underline{E}(\underline{C}^{\underline{N}})$	denote the expected cost of producing $\underline{Z}$ nondefective parts when $\underline{N}$ parts are started;
$\underline{S}$	denote the set-up cost;
$\underline{v}_1$	denote the labor and material cost per part on the first run;
$\underline{v}_2$	denote the labor and material cost per part on the second run;

$\underline{P}(\underline{N}\text{-}\underline{b} \geq \underline{Z})$ denote the probability that the nondefective parts produced on the first run are greater than or equal to what is required;

$\underline{P}(\underline{N}\text{-}\underline{b} < \underline{Z})$ denote the probability that the nondefective parts produced on the first run are less than what is required; and

$\underline{P}(\underline{N}\text{-}\underline{b} = \underline{Z}\text{-}\underline{i})$,
$\underline{i} = 1,2,\ldots,\underline{Z}$ denote the probability that the number of nondefective parts produced on the first run is $\underline{i}$ less than what is required.

The reader should be able to verify the following expression, in which each term represents the product of one of the different possible values of the random variable $\underline{C}^{\underline{N}}$ and its corresponding probability:

$$
\begin{aligned}
\underline{E}(\underline{C}^{\underline{N}}) &= (\underline{S} + \underline{v}_1\underline{N})\underline{P}(\underline{N}\text{-}\underline{b} \geq \underline{Z}) + (\underline{S} + \underline{v}_1\underline{N} + \underline{S} + \underline{v}_2)\underline{P}(\underline{N}\text{-}\underline{b} \\
&= \underline{Z} - 1) + (\underline{S} + \underline{v}_1\underline{N} + \underline{S} + 2\underline{v}_2)\underline{P}(\underline{N}\text{-}\underline{b} = \underline{Z} - 2) \\
&+ (\underline{S} + \underline{v}_1\underline{N} + \underline{S} + 3\underline{v}_2)\underline{P}(\underline{N}\text{-}\underline{b} = \underline{Z} - 3) \\
&+ \ldots + (\underline{S} + \underline{v}_1\underline{N} + \underline{S} + \underline{Z}\underline{v}_2)\underline{P}(\underline{N}\text{-}\underline{b} = \underline{Z} - \underline{Z}) \quad (6.3)
\end{aligned}
$$

Now

$$
\begin{aligned}
&(\underline{S} + \underline{v}_1\underline{N})[\underline{P}(\underline{N}\text{-}\underline{b} \geq \underline{Z}) + \underline{P}(\underline{N}\text{-}\underline{b} = \underline{Z} - 1) + \underline{P}(\underline{N}\text{-}\underline{b} = \underline{Z} - 2) + \ldots \\
&+ \underline{P}(\underline{N}\text{-}\underline{b} = \underline{Z} - \underline{Z})] = (\underline{S} + \underline{v}_1\underline{N})[\underline{P}(\underline{N}\text{-}\underline{b} \geq \underline{Z}) + \underline{P}(\underline{N}\text{-}\underline{b} < \underline{Z}] \\
&= (\underline{S} + \underline{v}_1\underline{N})(1)
\end{aligned}
$$

since $\underline{P}(\underline{N}\text{-}\underline{b} \geq \underline{Z}) + \underline{P}(\underline{N}\text{-}\underline{b} < \underline{Z})$ is a certain event. Thus by rearranging terms in Eq. 6.3 we obtain the following general formula:

$$
\begin{aligned}
\underline{E}(\underline{C}^{\underline{N}}) &= (\underline{S} + \underline{v}_1\underline{N})[\underline{P}(\underline{N}\text{-}\underline{b} \geq \underline{Z}) + \underline{P}(\underline{N}\text{-}\underline{b} = \underline{Z} - 1) \\
&+ \underline{P}(\underline{N}\text{-}\underline{b} = \underline{Z} - 2) + \ldots + \underline{P}(\underline{N}\text{-}\underline{b} = \underline{Z} - \underline{Z})] \\
&+ \underline{S}[\underline{P}(\underline{N}\text{-}\underline{b} = \underline{Z} - 1) + \underline{P}(\underline{N}\text{-}\underline{b} = \underline{Z} - 2) + \ldots \\
&+ \underline{P}(\underline{N}\text{-}\underline{b} = \underline{Z} - \underline{Z})] + \underline{v}_2\underline{P}(\underline{N}\text{-}\underline{b} = \underline{Z} - 1) \\
&+ 2\underline{v}_2\underline{P}(\underline{N}\text{-}\underline{b} = \underline{Z} - 2) + \ldots + \underline{Z}\underline{v}_2\underline{P}(\underline{N}\text{-}\underline{b} = \underline{Z} - \underline{Z}) \\
&= \underline{S} + \underline{v}_1\underline{N} + \underline{S}\underline{P}(\underline{N}\text{-}\underline{b} < \underline{Z}) + \underline{v}_2\underline{P}(\underline{N}\text{-}\underline{b} = \underline{Z} - 1) \\
&+ 2\underline{v}_2\underline{P}(\underline{N}\text{-}\underline{b} = \underline{Z} - 2) + \ldots + \underline{Z}\underline{v}_2\underline{P}(\underline{N}\text{-}\underline{b} = \underline{Z} - \underline{Z}) \quad (6.4)
\end{aligned}
$$

The reader should verify our preceding determination of $\underline{E}(\underline{C}^{17}) = 1,171$ using Eq. 6.4 .

6.3 SINGLE-CHANNEL QUEUING MODELS

We all have seen lines of people waiting for service at theater ticket windows, airline ticket counters, telephone booths, supermarket checkout counters, and factory tool cribs. Moreover, many of us have observed automobiles waiting to get past a highway toll booth, airplanes waiting for clearance to land, telephone calls waiting to get through a switchboard, and customers waiting for a product which is currently out of stock. All of these examples have two features in common. First, a person or object, e.g., automobile, airplane, telephone call, is waiting in line to receive a certain service. Second, these people or objects typically arrive at the service center at random, at least during certain specified intervals of time. A body of knowledge, called queuing theory, has been developed to treat examples of this type.

We shall introduce this theory by deriving some results for single channel queuing systems. By a queuing system, we mean the queue (the waiting line) and its associated service facility. A single channel queuing system is a system whose service facility can accommodate just one customer (one person or object) at a time. This system will observe the queue discipline, i.e., it will service customers on a first come first serve basis.

We shall be interested in certain characteristics of this system during the steady state, i.e., during that period of time in which the probability of there being n ($n = 0,1,2,\ldots$) customers in the system is stable and does not fluctuate with time. Specifically, we shall be interested in determining: 1) the probability of there being n people in the system at any point in time, 2) the rate of utilization of the service facility, 3) the expected number of customers in the system at any point in time, and 4) the expected time spent in the system by the average customer.

6.31 Probability of n People in the System.   In this section we shall derive, first, a formula which gives the probability of there being n ($n \geq 1$) customers in the queuing system at any point in time, and, second, a formula which gives the probability of there being $n = 0$ customers in the system. These probabilities will be denoted by $P(n)$, $n = 0,1,2,\ldots$.

Assume that we have defined a unit of time and that we have recorded the total number of customer arrivals at our service facility over several of these time units. We can then compute the average number (denoted by $\underline{A}$) of arrivals per unit of time. For example, if the unit of time is 1 minute, and if 800 customers arrived at random over a period of 200 minutes, then $\underline{A}$ = 800/200 = 4 customers arrive per minute on the average.

Now divide the time unit into $\underline{x}$ equal intervals, where $\underline{x} > \underline{A}$ and where each interval is so small that it is virtually impossible for more than one customer to arrive or depart in any one interval. Since arrivals occur at random over any time unit, since on the average $\underline{A}$ arrivals occur per time unit, and since in this time unit there are $\underline{x}$ opportunities for the event "an arrival" to occur, the probability of an arrival in any given interval is $\underline{A}/\underline{x}$. Since a customer either arrives or does not arrive during an interval, the probability of a customer not arriving is therefore $1 - \underline{A}/\underline{x}$.

Note that each interval is $1/\underline{x}$ of a time unit. For example, if $\underline{x}$ = 10 and the time unit is a minute, then each interval is $1/10$ of a minute.

Let $\underline{s}$ be a point in time and let $\underline{t}$ be another point in time equal to $\underline{s} + 1/\underline{x}$ time units; i.e., the interval $\underline{s}$ to $\underline{t}$ is $1/\underline{x}$ of a time unit long. From the preceding paragraphs, this means that at most one customer could arrive or depart during the interval $\underline{s} - \underline{t}$.

Finally, let $\underline{M}$ denote the average number of customers that can be serviced per unit of time if the service facility is never idle. As with $\underline{A}$, if a time unit is divided into $\underline{x}$ equal intervals, the probability of a customer leaving the system during any given interval is $\underline{M}/\underline{x}$, and the probability of his not leaving is $1 - \underline{M}/\underline{x}$.

What is the probability, denoted by $\underline{P}(\underline{n}_{\underline{t}})$, that $\underline{n}$ ($\underline{n} \geq 1$) customers will be in the queuing system at time $\underline{t}$? This event will occur only if one of the following four mutually exclusive events occurs: 1) $\underline{n}$ customers are in the system at time $\underline{s}$ and there are no arrivals and no departures during the time interval $\underline{s} - \underline{t}$; 2) $\underline{n}$ customers are in the system at $\underline{s}$ and there is 1 arrival and 1 departure during $\underline{s} - \underline{t}$; 3) $\underline{n} - 1$ customers are in the system at $\underline{s}$ and there is 1 arrival and 0 departures during $\underline{s} - \underline{t}$; 4) $\underline{n} + 1$ people are in the system at

$\underline{s}$ and there are 0 arrivals and 1 departure during $\underline{s} - \underline{t}$. Since arrivals and departures occur at random and are not influenced by what has occurred before, the probability of these four events can be determined from Eq. 5.5 . They are, respectively: (1) $\underline{P}(\underline{n}_s)(1 - \underline{A}/\underline{x})(1 - \underline{M}/\underline{x})$, (2) $\underline{P}(\underline{n}_s)(\underline{A}/\underline{x})(\underline{M}/\underline{x})$, (3) $\underline{P}(\underline{n} - 1_s)(\underline{A}/\underline{x})(1 - \underline{M}/\underline{x})$, (4) $\underline{P}(\underline{n} + 1_s)(1 - \underline{A}/\underline{x})(\underline{M}/\underline{x})$. Using Eq. 5.4 , we can obtain $\underline{P}(\underline{n}_t)$ by adding these four probabilities. Doing this addition, multiplying out each term, and then collecting terms yields

$$\underline{P}(\underline{n}_t) = \underline{P}(\underline{n}_s) + \underline{P}(\underline{n}_s)(1/\underline{x})(-\underline{A} - \underline{M}) + \underline{P}(\underline{n} - 1_s)(\underline{A}/\underline{x})$$

$$+ \underline{P}(\underline{n} + 1_s)(\underline{M}/\underline{x}) + 2\underline{P}(\underline{n}_s)(\underline{AM}/x^2)$$

$$- \underline{P}(\underline{n} - 1_s)(\underline{AM}/\underline{x}^2) - \underline{P}(\underline{n} + 1_s)(\underline{AM}/\underline{x}^2) \tag{6.5}$$

Now, by definition, in the steady state $\underline{P}(\underline{n}_t) = \underline{P}(\underline{n}_s)$; i.e., once a steady state is reached the probability of there being $\underline{n}$ customers in the system is the same regardless of the particular point in time considered in the steady state. Hence, if we subtract $\underline{P}(\underline{n}_t)$ [$= \underline{P}(\underline{n}_s)$] from both sides of Eq. 6.5 , and multiply the resulting equation by $\underline{x}$, we obtain

$$0 = \underline{P}(\underline{n}_s)(-\underline{A} - \underline{M}) + \underline{P}(\underline{n} - 1_s)\underline{A} + \underline{P}(\underline{n} + 1_s)\underline{M}$$

$$+ 2\underline{P}(\underline{n}_s)(\underline{AM}/\underline{x}) - \underline{P}(\underline{n} - 1_s)(\underline{AM}/\underline{x})$$

$$- \underline{P}(\underline{n} + 1_s)(\underline{AM}/\underline{x}) \tag{6.6}$$

Next, recall that $\underline{x}$ denotes the number of intervals into which we divided a time unit. $\underline{x}$ was to be sufficiently large (and therefore each interval sufficiently small) so that no more than one arrival or departure could occur within any interval. This implies that $\underline{x}$ must be an extremely large number. Since the last three terms in Eq. 6.6 are divided by $\underline{x}$ (which is a very large number), they must represent very small quantities (note that as $\underline{x} \to \infty$, $1/\underline{x}$, and hence each of these terms, approaches 0). Thus we can ignore these last three terms, and write Eq. 6.6 as

$$0 = \underline{P}(\underline{n}_{\underline{s}})(-\underline{A} - \underline{M}) + \underline{P}(\underline{n} - 1_{\underline{s}})\underline{A} + \underline{P}(\underline{n} + 1_{\underline{s}})\underline{M}$$

or, rearranging,

$$\underline{P}(\underline{n} + 1) = [(\underline{A} + \underline{M})/\underline{M}] \underline{P}(\underline{n})$$

$$- (\underline{A}/\underline{M})\underline{P}(\underline{n} - 1) \qquad\qquad \underline{n} \geq 1 \qquad\qquad (6.7)$$

Note that we have dropped the time subscripts ($\underline{s}$ and $\underline{t}$), since in the steady state the probability of $\underline{n}$ customers in the system is not affected by the particular point in time considered. Note also that Eq. 6.7 is only applicable for $\underline{n} \geq 1$.

To find $\underline{P}(\underline{n})$ for $\underline{n} = 0$, we follow a similar stream of analysis. This event will occur only if one of the two following mutually exclusive events occurs: 1) 0 customers are in the system at time $\underline{s}$ and no arrivals occur during $\underline{s} - \underline{t}$; 2) 1 customer is in the system at $\underline{s}$ and there are no arrivals and 1 departure during $\underline{s} - \underline{t}$. The probabilities of these events are given, respectively, by $\underline{P}(0_{\underline{s}})(1 - \underline{A}/\underline{x})$ and $\underline{P}(1_{\underline{s}})(1 - \underline{A}/\underline{x})(\underline{M}/\underline{x})$.

Following exactly the same procedure used in deriving Eq. 6.7, the reader can obtain

$$\underline{P}(1) = (\underline{A}/\underline{M})\underline{P}(0) \qquad\qquad (6.8)$$

Substituting Eq. 6.8 into Eq. 6.7 for $\underline{n} = 1$ yields

$$\underline{P}(2) = [(\underline{A} + \underline{M})/\underline{M}]\underline{P}(1) - (\underline{A}/\underline{M})\underline{P}(0) = (\underline{A}/\underline{M})^2 \underline{P}(0) \qquad (6.9)$$

Substituting Eq. 6.9 into Eq. 6.7 will yield $\underline{P}(3) = (\underline{A}/\underline{M})^3 \underline{P}(0)$. As the reader can verify, successive substitutions of this sort will give the result

$$\underline{P}(\underline{n}) = (\underline{A}/\underline{M})^{\underline{n}}\underline{P}(0) \qquad\qquad (6.10)$$

This means that once we determine $\underline{P}(0)$, any other $\underline{P}(\underline{n})$ can be determined directly from Eq. 6.10 .

To determine $\underline{P}(0)$, we note that $\underline{P}(0) + \underline{P}(1) + \underline{P}(2) \ldots = 1$ (the sum of the probabilities of all possible simple events is 1). This means that

$$\underline{P}(0) + (\underline{A}/\underline{M})\underline{P}(0) + (\underline{A}/\underline{M})^2 \underline{P}(0) + (\underline{A}/\underline{M})^3 \underline{P}(0) + \ldots = 1$$

or

$$\underline{P}(0) = 1/[1 + (\underline{A}/\underline{M}) + (\underline{A}/\underline{M})^2 + (\underline{A}/\underline{M})^3 + \ldots] \qquad (6.11)$$

Now we assume that $\underline{A} < \underline{M}$ (otherwise the average number of people arriving would exceed the average number capable of being serviced per unit of time and there would be no steady state, i.e., the number of people in the system would continually increase over time). Hence the denominator in Eq. 6.11 is the sum of an infinite geometric progression with constant ratio $0 < \underline{A}/\underline{M} < 1$. Therefore, from the well-known formula for this type of progression[1], the denominator becomes $1/[1 - (\underline{A}/\underline{M})] = \underline{M}/(\underline{M} - \underline{A})$. Substituting this expression in Eq. 6.11 we obtain

$$\underline{P}(0) = 1/[\underline{M}/(\underline{M} - \underline{A})] = 1 - (\underline{A}/\underline{M}) \qquad (6.12)$$

Thus, substituting Eq. 6.12 into Eq. 6.10 we finally find

$$\underline{P}(\underline{n}) = (\underline{A}/\underline{M})^{\underline{n}} [1 - (\underline{A}/\underline{M})] \qquad \underline{n} \geq 1 \qquad (6.13)$$

Eqs. 6.12 and 6.13 give the probability of there being $\underline{n}$ ($\underline{n} = 0,1,2,\dots$) customers in the queuing system at any point in time in the steady state.

6.32 Rate of Utilization of Service Facility. The service facility is idle whenever there are 0 people in the system. At any one point in time the probability of there being 0 people in the system is (from Eq. 6.12 $1 - (\underline{A}/\underline{M})$. Thus, if the system is checked many times, the fraction of the time that 0 people are found in it is $1 - (\underline{A}/\underline{M})$. This means that the fraction of the time that 1 or more people are found in the system is $1 - [1 - (\underline{A}/\underline{M})] = \underline{A}/\underline{M}$. Hence, the rate of utilization of the service facility (denoted by $\underline{U}$) is the ratio

$$\underline{U} = \underline{A}/\underline{M} \qquad (6.14)$$

---

[1] Let $a = \underline{A}/\underline{M}$. Then the denominator (denoted by $\underline{S}$) in Eq. 6.11 can be represented by $\underline{S} = 1 + \underline{a} + \underline{a}^2 + \underline{a}^3 + \dots + \underline{a}^{\underline{n}}$ (where $\underline{n} \to \infty$). Multiply this equation by $\underline{a}$, obtaining $\underline{Sa} = \underline{a} + \underline{a}^2 + \underline{a}^3 + \underline{a}^4 + \dots + \underline{a}^{\underline{n}+1}$, and subtract this new equation from the preceding equation:

$\underline{S} - \underline{Sa} = (1 + \underline{a} + \underline{a}^2 + \underline{a}^3 + \dots + \underline{a}^{\underline{n}}) - (\underline{a} + \underline{a}^2 + \underline{a}^3 + \underline{a}^4 + \dots + \underline{a}^{\underline{n}+1})$ or $\underline{S}(1 - \underline{a}) = 1 - \underline{a}^{\underline{n}+1}$ so that $\underline{S} = [1/(1 - \underline{a})] - [\underline{a}^{\underline{n}+1}/(1 - \underline{a})]$. But, since $0 < \underline{a} < 1$, as $\underline{n} \to \infty$ $\underline{a}^{\underline{n}+1} \to 0$, and the second term on the right hand side of the preceding equation vanishes. Hence $\underline{S} = 1/(1 - \underline{a}) = 1/[1 - (\underline{A}/\underline{M})]$.

6.33   Expected Number of Customers in the System.   The expected number of persons in the system (denoted by $\bar{n}$) at any point in time can be determined[2] from Eqs. 3.1 , 6.12 , and 6.13 as

$$\bar{n} = 0\underline{P}(0) + 1\underline{P}(1) + 2\underline{P}(2) + \dots$$

$$= 1\{(\underline{A}/\underline{M})[1 - (\underline{A}/\underline{M})]\} + 2\{(\underline{A}/\underline{M})^2[1 - (\underline{A}/\underline{M})]\} + \dots$$

$$= \underline{A}/(\underline{M} - \underline{A}) \tag{6.15}$$

6.34   Expected Time Spent in System by Average Person.   The expected time spent in the queuing system by the average person (denoted by $\underline{T}$) is derived as follows. In the steady state, the expected number of customers in the system is the constant $\bar{n}$ for any point in time that might be considered. Consider two points in time which are exactly one time unit apart. Since the expected number of customers in the system equals $\bar{n}$ at each of these points, and since on the average $\underline{A}$ customers arrive during this time interval, then on the average $\underline{A}$ customers must leave during this interval. Assume that the first of these two points in time corresponds exactly with the arrival of a customer. Since the expected number of persons in the system at this point is $\bar{n}$, this customer must be the $\bar{n}^{th}$ customer in the system. Thus, if $\underline{A}$ customers leave on the average during a unit of time, this customer will not be able to leave until $\bar{n}/\underline{A}$ time units have passed.

---

[2] $n = 0\underline{P}(0) + 1\underline{P}(1) + 2P(2) + \dots + \underline{n}P(\underline{n}) + \dots$

$= 1\{(A/M)[1-(A/M)]\} + 2\{(A/M)^2[1-(A/M)]\} + \dots + \underline{n}\{(\underline{A}/\underline{M})^n[1-(A/M)]\} + \dots$

$= (A/\bar{M})\overline{[1-(A/\bar{M})]}[1 + 2(A/\bar{M}) + 3(A/\bar{M})^2 + \dots + n(\overline{A/M})^{n-1} + \dots]$ (6.16)

Let $\underline{a} = \underline{A}/\underline{M}$. Then the sum in brackets, above, is $\underline{y}(\underline{a}) = [1 + 2\underline{a} + 3a^2 + \dots + n\underline{a}^{n-1} + \dots]$. Integrating $\underline{y}$ we obtain the sum of an infinite geometric progression $\underline{v}(\underline{a}) = \int \underline{y}(\underline{a})d\underline{a} = \underline{a} + \underline{a}^2 + \underline{a}^3 + \dots + \underline{a}^{\underline{n}} + \dots = \underline{a}/(1-\underline{a})$ (for $\underline{a} < 1$ or $\underline{A} < \underline{M}$; see footnote 1).

Differentiating $\underline{v}$ with respect to $\underline{a}$ yields $d\underline{v}/d\underline{a} = 1/(1 - \underline{a})^2 = y(\underline{a})$

Substituting this in Eq. 6.16 yields

$\bar{\underline{n}} = (\underline{A}/\underline{M})[1 - (\underline{A}/\underline{M})]\{1/[1 - (\underline{A}/\underline{M})]^2\} = \underline{A}/(\underline{M} - \underline{A})$

For example, if $\bar{n}$ = 12 customers and $\underline{A}$ = 4 customers per hour, when this customer arrives he typically will be the twelfth customer in the system. Since 4 customers leave on the average each time unit, 3 time units will pass before the twelfth customer is serviced. That is, this customer spends $\bar{n}/\underline{A}$ = 12/4 = 3 hours in the system.

Hence

$$\underline{T} = \bar{n}/\underline{A} = [\underline{A}/(\underline{M} - \underline{A})]/\underline{A} = 1/(\underline{M} - \underline{A}) \tag{6.17}$$

The following exercises will show how Eqs. 6.12 , 6.13 , 6.14 , 6.15 , and 6.17 aid management decision-making.

6.4 EXERCISES

1. Derive the expected costs shown in Table 6.2
2. In the example described in Section 6.2, determine the optimum number of parts to start if:

    (a) the original order is for 10 units,
    (b) the original order is for 20 units,
    (c) the percentage defective normally produced is .1,
    (d) $\underline{v}_2$ = 200,
    (e) $\underline{S}$ = 100.

3. Assume that at a factory tool crib, on the average, $\underline{A}$ = 12 workers arrive per hour requesting certain tools. Assume, further, that when the crib is in constant operation $\underline{M}$ = 60 workers, on the average, can be serviced per hour.

    (a) The factory manager follows a policy of adding an additional service facility whenever the probability of there being four or more workers in the system is greater than .5. Should he add another facility? [Hint: compute 1 - $\underline{P}$(0) - $\underline{P}$(1) - $\underline{P}$(2) - $\underline{P}$(3)].
    (b) The factory manager follows a policy of never opening up a service facility unless the rate of utilization will exceed .5. Should he close the present facility?

(c) The factory manager feels that, because of
crowding in the aisles, a new service facility
should be opened up whenever the expected
number of workers in the system exceeds 10.
Should he open up a new facility?

(d) Management feels that if the expected time spent
in the system by the average worker exceeds
.5 hours, it will pay to set up an additional service facility. Should such a facility be set up?

4. Answer questions 3a through 3d assuming that $\underline{A}$ = 9
and $\underline{M}$ = 10.

7 ▶ BINOMIAL PROBABILITY MODEL FOR ACCEPTANCE SAMPLING

7.1 MOTIVATION

In this chapter, we shall apply the binomial probability distribution to the problem of acceptance sampling, i.e., to the problem of deciding whether to accept or reject a shipment of goods on the basis of a sample of these goods. In presenting this application, we shall introduce the important concepts of hypothesis testing, type 1 and 2 errors, operating characteristic curves, sample design, double sampling, and AOQL.

Since a few of these concepts become somewhat involved, a set of exercises is provided at the end of each major section. Because these exercises contain additional theoretical material as well as practice problems, the reader is advised to complete these exercises before continuing to the next section.

7.2   HYPOTHESIS TESTING

Assume a firm must decide whether to accept a particular shipment of goods. If the shipment meets a certain quality standard, the firm would like to accept it. However, the firm cannot inspect the entire shipment to determine whether this standard is met because such an inspection would be too costly or too time-consuming. Moreover, even if cost and time are not deterrents to total inspection, the quality of the goods may be determinable only by destructive testing. For example, if the shipment contains rubber tires whose length of life is supposed to be 1,000 miles, the only way to check this specification may be to place a tire on a "road wear" testing machine and record the number of miles at which the tire wears out. Obviously, the entire shipment cannot be inspected in this way.

For these reasons, the firm decides to select and inspect a random sample of the goods. A hypothesis is formulated concerning the full shipment or population (the term population designates the entire group of items under study). This hypothesis is accepted or rejected depending on the results of the sample. The firm's decision will be governed by whether this hypothesis is accepted or rejected.

A hypothesis is accepted if the results of the sample are consistent with the hypothesis. If the sample results are inconsistent with the hypothesis, the hypothesis is rejected. The probability of obtaining the observed sample results, if the hypothesis is true, is the criterion for consistency between hypothesis and sample, i.e., is the criterion for accepting or rejecting hypotheses.

The higher the probability of obtaining the observed sample results, the more compatible are these results and the hypothesis. As this implies, we need to define a range of probabilities within which we shall say that a given probability is consistent with the hypothesis. We do this by defining the highest probability that lies outside this range. This probability is called the "significance level" or the "level of significance". For example, if the significance level were .05, sample results with a probability, denoted by $\underline{P}$, in the range $.05 < \underline{P} \leq 1.00$ would be said to be consistent with the hypothesis; any sample result with a probability of .05 or less would be considered inconsistent with the hypothesis. These comments can best be understood by an example.

<u>7.21 An Example</u>.   Suppose a manufacturer receives a ship-
ment of 1,000 electronic tubes and needs to decide whether
to accept or reject the lot on the basis of a sample taken at
random from the lot. Naturally, he would want to accept the
shipment if possible. However, in the present case, he decides that he cannot afford to accept it if he has reason to believe that the number of defective tubes is greater than 100 (if
more than ten percent are defective). His procedure is to assume that the shipment does contain exactly ten percent defective tubes. That is, he formulates the hypothesis that "the
shipment contains exactly ten percent defective tubes". Since
he decides to test this hypothesis by examining a sample of 10 tubes,
he calculates the probabilities that the sample will contain 0, 1,
2, . . ., 10 defective tubes. Next, he defines a level of significance, i.e., a probability (denoted by <u>a</u>) such that if the probability associated with the sample results is greater than <u>a</u> the
hypothesis, and therefore the lot, will be accepted, and if it is
equal to or less than <u>a</u>, the hypothesis, and lot, will be rejected.
Finally, he compares: 1) the probability associated with the
observed sample results and 2) the specified significance level <u>a</u>.

Columns 1 and 3 of Table 7.1 give the probabilities of <u>b</u> =
0,1, . . ., 10 defective tubes being found in a sample of 10 tubes
selected at random from the shipment of 1,000 tubes, assuming
that the shipment does contain 100 defective tubes. Since this
sampling procedure approximates a binomial experiment, these
probabilities [denoted by <u>P(b)</u>] are calculated from Eq. 5.6.
(The student should calculate some of these probabilities.)

Case 1.   Let us now assume that the sample contains 7 defective tubes. From Table 7.1, the probability of getting 7 or
more defective tubes in a sample of 10, drawn from a population
of 1,000 tubes containing 100 defective tubes, is .0000. It would,
in other words, be extremely unreasonable to believe, on the basis of this sample, that the shipment contains only 100 defective
tubes. It would be extremely likely to contain many more than
100 defective tubes. The rational decision would be to reject the
shipment.

Case 2.   Assume that the sample has 4 defective tubes. In
this case, Table 7.1 gives a value of .0112, which can be interpreted to mean we can expect 4 defectives in a sample of 10,

TABLE 7.1

PROBABILITY OF 0, 1, 2, . . . OR 10 DEFECTIVE TUBES
IN A SAMPLE OF 10 TUBES DRAWN AT RANDOM FROM
POPULATIONS IN WHICH 5 PERCENT, 10 PERCENT, AND
20 PERCENT ARE DEFECTIVE

b	$\underline{P(b)}$ for Defective Rate of		
	.05	.10	.20
0	.5987	.3487	.1074
1	.3152	.3874	.2684
2	.0746	.1937	.3020
3	.0105	.0574	.2013
4	.0009	.0112	.0881
5	.0001	.0015	.0264
6	.0000	.0001	.0055
7	.0000	.0000	.0008
8	.0000	.0000	.0001
9	.0000	.0000	.0000
10	.0000	.0000	.0000

under these conditions, about once in a hundred times. For 4
or more defective tubes, the probability is .0128. (Why?)

Without further information, we can come to either one of
two conclusions: 1) The probability of getting 4 or more defective tubes in this case is quite small and therefore, having obtained 4 in our sample, we must conclude that the hypothesis
that there are 100 defective tubes in the lot is false. Most likely,
there are more .   2) In this case, the observed results could
be expected to occur a little more than once in a hundred times,
and this isn't so bad. The occurrence of 4 defective tubes in
the sample is compatible with the hypothesis.

To decide which of these two arguments to accept, we need
to define a significance level. In practice, significance levels
are usually defined to lie between .001 and .100, the most common levels being .05 and .01. If we decide to employ a significance level of .05, since the probability, viz., .0128, of the observed sample results or results even more extreme is less
than .05, the hypothesis (and shipment) would be rejected.

Case 3.   Assume there is one defective tube in the sample. From Table 7.1, if the hypothesis is true, the probability of one or more defective tubes occurring in a sample of 10 is .6513 . Evidently the sample results are quite consistent with the hypothesis, because one would expect a sample to have at least one defective tube about 65 out of a hundred times. The lot is therefore acceptable under this state of affairs.

7.22 Exercises

1.   Show that if the shipment were assumed to have more than ten percent, say twenty percent, defective tubes, it would be more likely that a sample of 10 could have 7 defective tubes.

2. Show that if the shipment were assumed to have less than ten percent, say five percent, defective tubes, it would be less likely that a sample of 10 would contain 3 defective tubes. As this implies, if the hypothesis is rejected when the population percentage defective is assumed to be ten percent it will always be rejected, since the relevant probability will always be smaller, for populations in which the percentage defective is assumed to be less than ten percent. This is why we can test the hypothesis that the percentage defective in the population is no more than ten percent simply by testing whether it is exactly ten percent.

3. In case 2, what decision is made if the significance level is .01? If it is .1?

4. In the situations described in this section, suppose 5 tubes were defective in the sample. Assume a significance level and decide whether to accept or reject the lot.

5. In the last census, forty percent of the voters in a particular city were registered Republicans. A sample of twenty voters is selected at random today, and sixteen are found to be Republicans. Would you say that the percentage of voters who are Republicans has increased? Use a five percent significance level. (Ans.: Yes, probability of sixteen or more Republicans is .0003 if the percentage of voters who are Republicans is forty percent).

6. Last year a complete survey of housewives in the Boston area showed that thirty percent preferred Brand X coffee to any other. This year a sample of eight housewives from the same area contains two housewives who prefer Brand X. Employing a one percent significance level, would you conclude that the percentage of housewives who prefer Brand X has decreased? (Ans.: No; probability of two or fewer favorable answers is .5518 if the percentage of housewives favoring Brand X is thirty percent).

7. When a market research firm includes a nickel with its mailed questionnaire, it finds that sixty percent of the questionnaires are returned. As an experiment, it selects ten additional names at random and mails the same questionnaire to these people, including a quarter instead of a nickel. Nine of these questionnaires are returned. Employing a one percent significance level, would you conclude that the inclusion of a nickel results in a better response?

8. A manufacturer produces lots of metal parts, each lot containing 3,000 parts. To maintain the quality of his product, he decides to reprocess any lot which shows evidence of being more than five percent defective. In a sample of twelve parts, one is defective. If he employs a .1 percent significance level, should the lot be reprocessed?

7.3 TYPE 1 ERRORS

In the preceding section, the decision to accept or reject the shipment was based on testing the hypothesis that the shipment contains no more than ten percent defective tubes. It should be clear to the student that errors can result from the procedure described. If the hypothesis were actually false, and the shipment had more than ten percent defective tubes, the sample result could still lead to the acceptance of the hypothesis. For example, if the percentage defective were actually twenty percent, a sample containing 0 or 1 defective items could result, thereby leading to the acceptance of a shipment which should be rejected. Similarly, if the hypothesis were actually true, the sample results could lead to its rejection (e.g., a sample containing 7 defectives could conceivably come from a lot which is .05 defective). Thus, the problem the manufacturer confronts is twofold: 1) What is the probability that a hypothesis H, which in fact happens to be true, will be rejected? 2) What is the probability that a hypothesis H, which in fact happens to be false, will be accepted?

These considerations lead to the following definition:

> Definition 7.1: When a hypothesis H, which is in fact true, is rejected, a type 1 error has occurred. The probability of a type 1 error is denoted by a.

To take an example, assume a manufacturer has decided to accept a shipment of tubes if it is not more than ten percent defective. If we let d designate the hypothetical percentage defective in the population, d = .10 in the present case. He adopts the acceptance sampling plan that if a sample of n = 10 tubes taken at random contains no more than c = 2 defective tubes, he will accept the lot. If more than 2 defective tubes are found, he will reject the lot, and, thereby, the hypothesis that the shipment is no more than ten percent defective. Evidently, if the sample contained only one defective tube the lot would be accepted. The greatest number of defective items allowed without leading to a rejection of the hypothesis is called the acceptance number. This number is designated by the letter c. An acceptance sampling plan involves the specification of a sample size n and an acceptance number c. What is the probability of rejecting the hypothesis if the percentage defective, d, is .10?

From Table 7.1, we know that the probability of obtaining 3 or more defective tubes in a sample of 10 tubes, if the lot did contain exactly d = ten percent defective, is .0792. This means that if many such lots were submitted, 7.92 percent would contain 3 or more defective tubes. Having decided to reject a lot if 3 or more defective tubes are discovered in a sample of 10 taken at random, the manufacturer could expect to reject 7.92 percent of such lots submitted in the long run. Since he actually wants to accept a lot if it is exactly ten percent defective, he would be making a wrong decision. He would be committing a type 1 error, since he would be rejecting the hypothesis that the lot is exactly ten percent defective when in fact the lot is exactly ten percent defective. The probability a of committing this type 1 error is .0792.

To take another example, assuming the same acceptance sampling plan (i.e., n = 10, c = 2), what is the probability of committing a type 1 error if five percent of the population is defective? The probability of obtaining 3 or more defective tubes, in a sample of 10 tubes, is .0115 (see Table 7.1). The probability of committing a type 1 error is therefore a = .0115.

These two examples demonstrate that the probability of committing a type 1 error for a given sampling plan decreases as the percentage of defective tubes in the population decreases.

7.31 Exercises

1. If the acceptance number for a given sample size is increased, the probability of a type 1 error (for

any specified d) decreases. Show this is the case by comparing the preceding examples where the acceptance number was
2, with the following: The acceptance number is 3 for a sample
of 10 tubes from a shipment which is ten percent defective.
Find a, the probability of a type 1 error.

2. The probability of a type 1 error for a given acceptance
number increases as the sample size increases. Show this is so
by comparing previous examples with the following problem: if
no more than 2 defective tubes are found in a sample of 15 tubes
selected at random from the shipment, the hypothesis that the
lot is ten percent defective will be accepted, otherwise rejected.
We assume the lot to be, in fact, ten percent defective. Find a,
the probability of a type 1 error.

3. A manufacturer is willing to accept lots which are as
much as five percent defective, but wishes to reject lots which
are more than five percent defective. An item is defective if its
breaking strength is less than 100 pounds per square inch. It is
tested by applying pressure and recording the value at which it
breaks. Since the sampling process is destructive, 100 percent
sampling is, of course, out of the question. Furthermore, since
the dollar value of each item is very high relative to the cost of
the finished product of which it is a part, only small samples are
feasible. The manufacturer adopts the following sampling plan:
return the entire lot if, in a sample of five items, more than one
is defective. Find a if the percentage defective in the population
is actually five percent, one percent, ten percent.

4. In the above problem, assume that the percentage defective in the population is five percent and that the acceptance number is still 1. What is the probability of a type 1 error if the
sample size is 4? 8? What happens to a as the sample size increases?

5. In the above problem, assume that the sample size is 5
and that the percentage defective in the population is five percent.
What is the probability of a type 1 error if the acceptance number
is 0? 2? What happens to a as the acceptance number increases?

7.4   TYPE 2 ERRORS

We start this section with the following definition:

Definition 7.2: When a hypothesis H, which in fact is false, is accepted, a type 2 error has been committed. The probability of a type 2 error is denoted by B.

To take an example, assume that our manufacturer adopts the following plan. He takes a random sample of 10 tubes and will accept the entire lot if no more than 2 of the tubes in the sample are defective. We know that he wants to return all lots which are actually more than ten percent defective. His hypothesis is that the lot is ten percent defective. Assume that a lot which is in fact twenty percent defective is submitted. It is quite possible that a sample of ten tubes will contain none, one, or two defective tubes. In each of these cases, the stated sampling plan will lead to the acceptance of the hypothesis that the population from which this sample was taken is ten percent defective, and the entire lot will, accordingly, be retained. But, by assumption, the percentage defective in the population is twenty percent, and the entire lot should be returned. Because the stated sampling plan led to the acceptance of a hypothesis which is in fact false, a type 2 error is committed.

Case 1.   In the situation just described, what is the probability of committing a type 2 error? From Table 7.1 (columns 1 and 4), the probability of obtaining 2 or fewer defective tubes, in a sample of 10 selected from a population containing twenty percent defectives, is .6778. Thus, the probability of making a type 2 error is .6778, i.e., B = .6778.

Case 2.   Employing the sampling plan just described, find B if the percentage defective in the population is thirty percent. The probability of obtaining 2 or fewer defective tubes, in a sample of 10 selected at random from a population in which the percentage defective is exactly thirty percent, is .3828.

Cases 1 and 2 illustrate the following relationship. For a stated sampling plan, the greater the amount by which the actual percentage defective in the population exceeds the hypothetical percentage defective, the smaller the probability of incurring a type 2 error.

Case 3.   The following sampling plan is adopted: in a sample of 10 tubes, if no more than 3 defective tubes are obtained, the entire lot will be accepted. What is the probability of making a type 2 error if the population percentage defective is twenty percent?   The probability of obtaining 3 or fewer defectives in a sample of 10 is .8791.

Cases 1 and 3 illustrate the fact that, for a fixed sample size and population percentage defective, the probability of committing a type 2 error (i.e., B) increases as the acceptance number increases. For example, when the sample size and population percentage defective were, respectively, ten and twenty percent, B, the probability of a type 2 error, increased from .6778 to .8791 as the acceptance number increased from 2 to 3.

Case 4.   The following sampling plan is adopted. In a sample of 15 tubes, if no more than 2 defectives are found, the entire lot will be accepted. If the population percentage defective is twenty percent, find B. The probability of obtaining 2 or fewer defective tubes in a sample of 15 tubes is .3980. Therefore B = .3980.

Cases 1 and 4 thus illustrate the following relationship. For a given acceptance number and population percentage defective, the probability of a type 2 error decreases as the sample size increases.

7.41 Exercises

1. For the problem situation depicted in Exercise 3 of section 7.31, what is the probability of a type 2 error if the percentage defective in the population is actually five percent? one percent? ten percent?

2. Answer Exercise 4 of Section 7.31, substituting type 2 for type 1 errors.

3. Answer Exercise 5 of Section 7.31, substituting type 2 for type 1 errors.

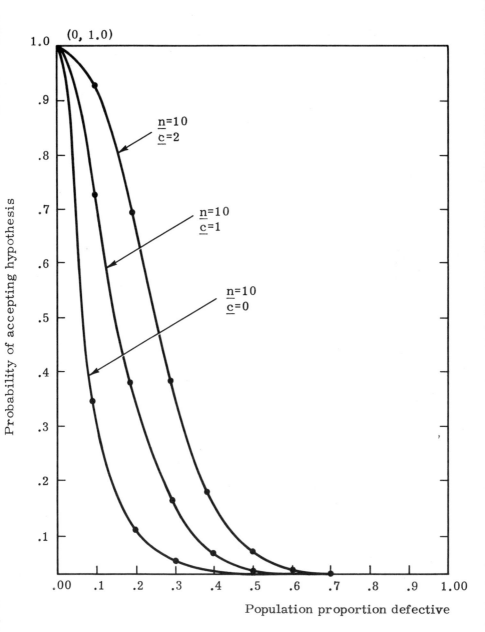

Figure 7.1 Operating characteristic curves for different
acceptance numbers

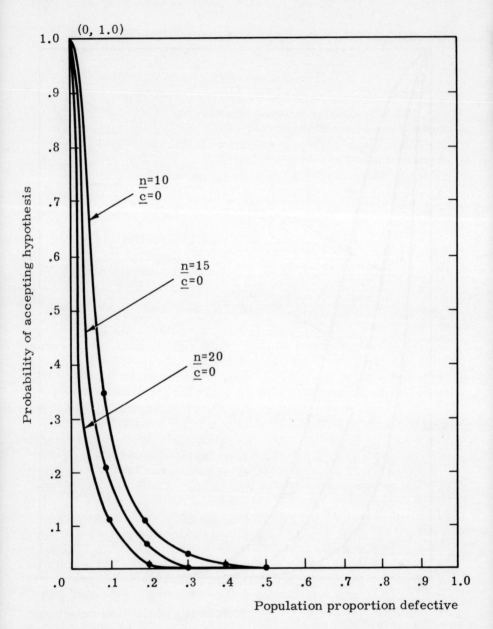

Figure 7.2 Operating characteristic curves for different sample sizes

7.5   THE OPERATING CHARACTERISTIC CURVE

Up to now, we have discussed, for a specified type of error, the nature of the relationship between the probability of that error and the acceptance number, the sample size, and the population percentage defective. In this section we shall examine the relationship between the two types of errors. The most useful tool for this purpose is the operating characteristic (OC) curve.

> Definition 7.3: The operating characteristic curve for a given sampling plan is the graph of the relationship between the set of possible population percentages defective and the set of probabilities of accepting the submitted lot.

To illustrate this definition, we shall construct an OC curve for a sampling plan in which the sample size n = 10 and the acceptance number c = 1. The required set of points can be obtained by employing Eq. 5.6 for different d's with n taken as 10 and c as 1. For each d we calculate the probability of accepting the submitted lot, i.e., we calculate the probability of obtaining either 0 or 1 defectives. If we let m denote the number of defectives, then $P(m \leq c)$ denotes the probability that $m \leq c$. Table 7.2 shows the results of these calculations for 12 selected points.

We now plot these points on a graph. Along the x axis (the horizontal axis) in Fig. 7.1 we measure the population proportion defective in tenths, and along the y axis (the vertical axis) we measure the probability of accepting the hypothesis, also given in tenths. The middle curve in Figure 7.1 is the result of connecting the graph of Table 7.1 by a smooth line. The set of all points on this curve is the graph of the sampling plan for n = 10 and c = 1, i.e., the OC curve for this plan. The reader should notice that the curve decreases as we move from left to right.

As a further example, we now construct the OC curve for a sampling plan in which n = 20 and c = 0. Table 7.3 shows 12 selected d's with n = 20 and c = 0. The curve closest to the origin in Figure 7.2 shows the results of connecting these points with a smoothed curve.

TABLE 7.2

SELECTED POINTS ON THE OC CURVE CORRESPONDING TO n = 10, c = 1

Population Percentage Defective d	Probability of Acceptance $P(m \leq c)$
.00	1.0000
.05	.9139
.10	.7361
.20	.3758
.30	.1493
.40	.0464
.50	.0107
.60	.0017
.70	.0001
.80	.0000
.90	.0000
1.00	.0000

Figures 7.1 and 7.2 present the OC curves for 6 different sampling plans. These figures clearly illustrate the results implied in the examples of the preceding sections. The following discussion will show how to interpret these figures. First we consider type 2 errors.

7.51 Relationship between B and d, c, and n. Since, for a given sampling plan, the OC curve shows the probability of accepting the hypothesis for any specified population percentage defective, the probability, B, of making a type 2 error can be read along the vertical axis for all possible population percentage defectives. For example, assume we formulate the hypothesis that the sample selected comes from a population which is no more than ten percent defective. For any of the six sampling plans, the probability of making a type 2 error when the population percentage defective is ten percent or less (represented by the points on the horizontal axis between .00 and .1) is 0. To find the probability of a type 2 error for a specific sampling plan

TABLE 7.3

SELECTED POINTS ON THE OC CURVE
CORRESPONDING TO $\underline{n}$ = 20, $\underline{c}$ = 0

Population Percentage Defective $\underline{d}$	Probability of Acceptance $\underline{P(m \leq s)}$
.00	1.0000
.05	.3585
.10	.1216
.20	.0115
.30	.0008
.40	.0000
.50	.0000
.60	.0000
.70	.0000
.80	.0000
.90	.0000
1.00	.0000

when the population percentage defective is greater than ten percent, we find the point, on the OC curve for this sampling plan, whose abscissa ($\underline{x}$ coordinate) is the given population percentage defective, and read its ordinate ($\underline{y}$ coordinate). For example, the OC curve for $\underline{n}$ = 10, $\underline{c}$ = 2 (Fig. 7.1) shows that when $\underline{d}$ = .3, $\underline{B}$ = .38.

The probability of a type 2 error, for a given sampling plan, decreases as the population percentage defective increases (as pointed out before the OC curve slopes downward from left to right). Also, if a vertical line is erected in Figure 7.1 at a population proportion defective of, say, .2, it can be seen that, for a fixed sample size, the probability of a type 2 error increases as the acceptance number increases. Moreover, if a vertical line is erected in Figure 7.2 at, say, the same population percentage defective, it can be seen that, for a fixed acceptance number, the probability of a type 2 error increases as the sample size decreases.

7.52   Relationship between a and d, c, and n.   Now we turn to a consideration of type 1 errors. If the probability of accepting the hypothesis (read along the vertical axis) is P, then clearly the probability of rejecting it is 1-P. Therefore, the distance from the point (0,1) to any point on the vertical axis represents the probability of rejecting the hypothesis. If the hypothesis is actually true, this distance can be taken as a, the probability of a type 1 error.

Assume, still, that we have formulated the hypothesis that the sample selected comes from a population which is no more than ten percent defective. For all six sampling plans, when the population percentage defective is more than ten percent, the probability of a type 1 error, given by the horizontal axis for all values higher than ten percent, is 0. For a specific sampling plan, the probability of a type 1 error, when the population percentage defective is ten percent or less, is then directly proportional to the vertical distance between the relevant point on the required OC curve and the horizontal line erected at the ordinate of 1.00.

As before, the probability of a type 1 error, for a given sampling plan, decreases as the population proportion defective decreases. Also, Figure 7.1 shows that for a fixed sample size the probability of a type 1 error decreases as the acceptance number increases [erect a vertical line at a population proportion defective of, say, .05 and compare the vertical distance along this line between each curve and the line perpendicular to the vertical axis at point (0,1)]. Figure 7.2 shows that for a fixed acceptance number the probability decreases as the sample size decreases (erect another vertical line to see this).

7.53   Relationship between a, B, and n.   In addition to illustrating the results of the preceding sections, Figures 7.1 and 7.2 show the relationship between the probabilities of type 1 and type 2 errors and sample size. For example, assume that the sample selected actually comes from a lot which is twenty percent defective. For a fixed sample size, the probability of making a type 2 error can only be reduced by reducing the acceptance number (see Figure 7.1). But this downward shift of OC curves necessarily lengthens the vertical line between the relevant OC curve and the horizontal line at the ordinate (1.0), thereby increasing the probability of a type 1 error. Similarly, the probability of a type 1 error cannot be reduced, for a fixed sample

size, without a simultaneous increase in the probability of a
type 2 error. Furthermore, Figure 7.2 shows that for a fixed
acceptance number, the probability of one type of error can
only be decreased at the expense of the other.

However, Figure 7.3 shows that if both the acceptance number and the sample size are increased, the probabilities of both
types of errors will decrease. For example, if we are testing
the hypothesis that a particular sample comes from a population with a percentage defective of no more than approximately
thirteen percent, when the sample size and acceptance number
are raised, respectively, from 10 and 0 to 20 and 1, the probability of both types of errors decreases. This follows because
the OC curve corresponding to the larger n and c: 1) lies below the other OC curve, and thus has a smaller B for d > .13;
and 2) lies above the other OC curve, and thus has a smaller
a, for d < .13. As this illustration implies, the probabilities of
both types of errors, for a stated hypothesis, can be made as
low as desired, provided only that the sample size and acceptance number be made sufficiently large.

7.6   DETERMINATION OF c FOR SPECIFIED n AND a

The operating characteristic curves of Figures 7.1, 7.2,
and 7.3 illustrate the basic relationships between n, c, d, a, and
B. The discussion which follows will show how a knowledge of
these relationships can be employed to develop rational sampling plans. The examples of this section have been constructed
in order to illustrate the manner in which the initial approach to
the problem differs from that employed in previous examples.
In these earlier examples, c and n were specified first' and then
a and B were determined. The cases which immediately follow
show how, for a fixed n, a is first specified and then c is determined. The following section demonstrates the general proce -
dure that would be employed in practice, viz., a and B are first
specified and then c and n are determined.

Case 1.   Assume that a sample of 10 tubes is selected at
random from a lot of 10,000. The manufacturer decides that
he is willing to accept the lot only if he has reason to believe

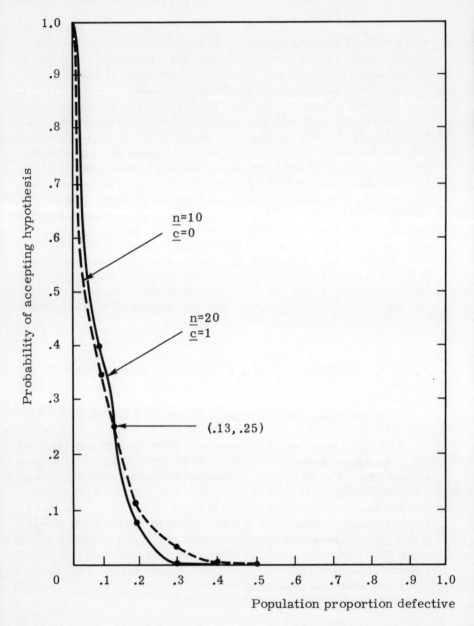

Figure 7.3 Operating characteristic curves for two sample plans

that $\underline{d}$, the percentage defective in the population or lot, is no greater than .05. What is the smallest possible acceptance number such that $\underline{a}$ ≤ .08?

Applying Eq. 5.6, we find (first two columns of Table 7.1) that when $\underline{c}$ = 1 and $\underline{d}$ = .05, $\underline{a}$ = .0861; when $\underline{c}$ = 2 and $\underline{d}$ = .05, $\underline{a}$ = .0115. From Exercise 1 of Section 7.31, we know that, for a fixed $\underline{d}$ and $\underline{n}$, as $\underline{c}$ increases $\underline{a}$ decreases. Therefore, in this case, $\underline{c}$ = 2 is the smallest acceptance number for which $\underline{a}$ is less than or equal to .08 when $\underline{d}$ is exactly equal to .05.

From the end of Section 7.3, we know that $\underline{a}$ decreases, for a given sampling plan (for a fixed $\underline{n}$ and $\underline{c}$) as $\underline{d}$ decreases. Therefore, $\underline{c}$ = 2 is also the smallest acceptance number for which $\underline{a}$ ≤ .08 when $\underline{d}$ ≤ .05; i.e., if $\underline{d}$ were actually smaller than .05, $\underline{a}$ would be even less than .0115 for this sampling plan.

Note that any $\underline{c}$ ≥ 2 will satisfy the specified requirements concerning the size of $\underline{a}$. We are particularly concerned with the smallest possible $\underline{c}$ value which satisfies these requirements because we know (from Cases 1 and 3 of Section 7.4) that, for a fixed $\underline{n}$, the smaller $\underline{c}$ is the smaller $\underline{B}$ is.

Now for this sampling plan, what is $\underline{B}$ when $\underline{d}$ ≥ .25? Note, from Eq. 5.6, that for $\underline{d}$ = .25 (and $\underline{n}$ = 10, $\underline{c}$ = 2) we have $\underline{B}$ = .5256. We know (from Cases 1 and 2 of Section 7.4) that $\underline{B}$ decreases, for a fixed sampling plan, as $\underline{d}$ increases. Therefore, $\underline{B}$ ≤ .5256 when $\underline{d}$ ≥ .25 .

Case 2.   Now assume a sample of 15 tubes is selected at random. What is the smallest possible acceptance number that $\underline{a}$ ≤ .08 when $\underline{d}$ ≤ .05? For this sampling plan, what is $\underline{B}$ when $\underline{d}$ ≥ .25?

In this case, when $\underline{c}$ = 1 and $\underline{d}$ = .05, $\underline{a}$ = .1710; when $\underline{c}$ = 2 and $\underline{d}$ = .05, $\underline{a}$ = .0362. Thus $\underline{c}$ = 2 is again the acceptance number we are seeking. Notice, however, that for this sampling plan, $\underline{B}$ ≤ .2361 when $\underline{d}$ ≥ .25. Thus when $\underline{n}$ is increased from 10 to 15 and $\underline{c}$ is held constant at 2, $\underline{a}$ (for $\underline{d}$ ≤ .05) increases slightly from .0115 to .0362 while $\underline{B}$ (for $\underline{d}$ ≥ .25) decreases significantly from .5256 to .2361.

7.7   SAMPLE DESIGN

We now have all the concepts necessary for a rational approach to the overall design of an efficient sampling plan. Such a plan is one that keeps the dollar cost of obtaining the sample, and therefore the sample size, as low as possible, consistent with a set of established error limits.

To illustrate the procedure, assume that the manufacturer to whom we have constantly alluded wishes to know what size sample will: 1) keep his sampling dollar cost as low as possible, 2) result in a .08 or less probability of rejecting a true hypothesis when the population percentage defective is .05 or less, and 3) result in a .10 or less probability of accepting a false hypothesis when the population percentage defective is .25 or more. In other words, he seeks the smallest n that will yield: 1) a ≤ .08 when d ≤ .05, and 2) B ≤ .10 when d ≥ .25 .

A trial and error solution will be employed, the general procedure being as follows: First, any sample size, e.g., n = 10, is arbitrarily selected. Second, the minimum c such that a ≤ .08 when d ≤ .05 is derived, according to the technique illustrated in the examples of the previous section. Third, B, when d ≥ .25, is determined for this sampling plan. Fourth, if B is > .10 the first three steps are repeated for another (larger) arbitrarily selected n. This sequence of steps is repeated for different sample sizes until one, designated by n', is obtained such that a ≤ .08 and B ≤ .10 for n', and a ≤ .08 and B > .10 for $n' - 1$.

Table 7.4 summarizes these computations for four arbitrarily selected samples.

The desired sampling plan is seen to be one in which n = 20 and c = 2, a = .0755, and B = .0913. The next smallest sample size ($n'-1$ = 19) yields an a = .0665 and B = .1113. The fact that c = 2 for all four plans is a peculiarity associated with this particular example; normally, c will increase as n increases, at least after a point. In the present case, since a has increased from .0115 to just under .08 as n has increased from 10 to 20, it appears that an n of 21 or 22 should require a c of 3 in order for a to be less than or equal to .08 when d ≤ .05.

We summarize the results of this chapter thus far. In many business situations decisions must be made under conditions of uncertainty. In particular, in acceptance sampling applications, decisions relating to a population must be made on the basis of a randomly selected sample, typically containing relatively few elements from the population. A hypothesis concerning this unknown population is made, and then tested by statistically examining this sample. It is important to know that two types of in-

TABLE 7.4

DETERMINATION OF THE SAMPLING PLAN
WITH THE MINIMUM $\underline{n}$ SUCH THAT

1. $\underline{a} \leq .08$ WHEN $\underline{d} \leq .05$
AND
2. $\underline{B} \leq .10$ WHEN $\underline{d} \geq .25$

Sampling Plan	$\underline{a}$ (for $\underline{d}$ = .05)	$\underline{B}$ (for $\underline{d}$ = .25)
A. $\underline{n} = 10$, $\underline{c} = 1$	.0861	.2440
$\underline{n} = 10$, $\underline{c} = 2$	.0115	.5256
B. $\underline{n} = 15$, $\underline{c} = 1$	.1710	.0802
$\underline{n} = 15$, $\underline{c} = 2$	.0362	.2361
C. $\underline{n} = 19$, $\underline{c} = 1$	.2453	.0310
$\underline{n} = 19$, $\underline{c} = 2$	.0665	.1113
D. $\underline{n} = 20$, $\underline{c} = 1$	.2642	.0243
$\underline{n} = 20$, $\underline{c} = 2$	.0755	.0913

correct conclusions can be drawn from this statistical examination; it is even more important to know that the probabilities of
incurring these errors can be made as small as desired, pro -
vided only that the sample size is made sufficiently large.

While these results have been inferred from examples
taken from the area of acceptance sampling, they are applicable to all fields of business and economics, since these examples can be used as models for similarly structured problems. In fact, they are quite generally applicable to all fields
of scientific inquiry. Statistical hypotheses are formulated and
tested, as indicated above, in all of the physical, social, and
engineering sciences. The following example and exercises
will present illustrative examples from fields other than the
specialized one of acceptance sampling.

7.71 Marketing Example.   Last year, twenty percent of the
people in State A favored Product X. In order to determine the
allocation of advertising funds throughout the country, a market researcher formulates the hypothesis that $\underline{d}$, the percentage
of people in State A favoring Product X this year, is no more
than twenty percent. What is the smallest sample he can select
to test this hypothesis, given that $\underline{a} \leq .09$ when $\underline{d} \leq .20$ and
$\underline{B} \leq .06$ when $\underline{d} \geq .50$?

TABLE 7.5

DETERMINATION OF THE SAMPLING PLAN
WITH THE MINIMUM $\underline{n}$ SUCH THAT

1. $\underline{a} \leq .09$ WHEN $\underline{d} \leq .20$
AND
2. $\underline{B} \leq .06$ WHEN $\underline{d} \geq .50$

Sampling Plan	$\underline{a}$ (for $\underline{d} = .20$)	$\underline{B}$ (for $\underline{d} = .50$)
A. $\underline{n} = 19, \underline{c} = 5$	.1631	.0318
$\underline{n} = 19, \underline{c} = 6$	.0676	.0835
B. $\underline{n} = 20, \underline{c} = 5$	.1958	.0207
$\underline{n} = 20, \underline{c} = 6$	.0867	.0577

Table 7.5 summarizes, for two sampling plans, the results of following the procedure utilized in the solution to the preceding example. We see that the desired sampling plan is $\underline{n} = 20$ and $\underline{c} = 6$, with $\underline{a} = .0867$ and $\underline{B} = .0577$.

7.72 Exercises

1. If a manufacturing process is working correctly, fifteen percent of the items turned out will be defective. However, it is quite costly to check this process since it involves a shut-down of the entire plant for an extended period of time. On the other hand, if $\underline{d}$ is greater than .15 the extra cost incurred is relatively slight, and, in fact, makes no noticeable difference in costs as long as $\underline{d}$ does not exceed .25. The manufacturer formulates the hypothesis that the process is working correctly. In this case, it is very important for the manufacturer to avoid a type 1 error. Design a sampling plan in which $\underline{a} \leq .01$ when $\underline{d} \leq .15$, and $\underline{B} \leq .20$ when $\underline{d} \geq .25$.

2. When Drug X contains more than ten percent of Ingredient Y, users of the drug can become severely ill. On the other hand, when the drug contains ten percent or less of this ingredient, the drug produces no ill effects. Furthermore, the cost of reprocessing a batch is relatively small. A hypothesis that the drug produces no ill effects is formulated. In this case, the manufacturer is very anxious to avoid a type 2 error (why?) and not overly concerned about a type 1 error (why?). Accordingly, he would like to know the minimum $\underline{n}$

such that $\underline{a} \leq .40$ when $\underline{d} \leq .10$, and $\underline{B} \leq .0001$ when $\underline{d} \geq .15$. Determine the required sampling plan.

3. In a preview showing of a new model automobile last year, at least eighty percent of the persons in the "over 40" age group favored the new model. This year, the automobile manufacturer would like to know if the same degree of preference exists in this age group for this year's model. If it does, he can use the same promotional strategy as last year; otherwise, he will have to devise a new one. He poses the hypothesis that no more than eighty percent of the persons in the "over 40" age group favor the new model, and wishes to test it by obtaining a random sample of persons in this age group at the current showing. If a type 1 error is made, this will not lead to a change in promotional expenditures allocated to this age group (since presumably they still like the car to the same extent), and this could lead to a disastrous and unnecessary fall in sales. A type 2 error, on the other hand, will not result in a fall in sales merely because of promotional strategy. Accordingly, the manufacturer wishes to keep the risk of a type 1 error relatively low. What is the smallest sample which has $\underline{a} \leq .01$ when $\underline{d} \leq .80$, and $\underline{B} \leq .15$ when $\underline{d} \geq .90$?

4. A market research firm knows, from past experience, that when a nickel is enclosed in a certain type of questionnaire at most thirty percent of the questionnaires are returned. The firm wishes to test the hypothesis that when a quarter is enclosed in the questionnaire, at most thirty percent of the questionnaires will be returned. What sample size is required so that $\underline{a} \leq .05$ when $\underline{d} \leq .30$ and $\underline{B} \leq .05$ when $\underline{d} \geq .50$?

5. A television manufacturer purchases a particular type of tube from an outside supplier. The supplier states that no more than five percent of the tubes shipped at any one time will be defective. The manufacturer wants to make certain that each shipment meets this specification, because if more than five percent of the tubes are defective his service department will not be able to handle the number of TV sets that will be returned for repair. Furthermore, if too many sets have to be returned his reputation will be damaged. A large lot of tubes is received. A sample is selected at random and specially tested to determine how many tubes are defective. The hypothesis that the lot contains no more than five percent defective tubes is formulated. In this case, the manufacturer wishes to minimize the risk of a type 2 error. What sample size is necessary in order for $\underline{a} \leq .20$ when $\underline{d} \leq .05$ and for $\underline{B} \leq .001$ when $\underline{d} \geq .10$?

7.8   DOUBLE SAMPLING

The discussion relating to acceptance sampling has so far been concerned solely with single sampling plans, i.e., a single sample from a lot was the basis for the decision to accept or reject the entire lot. In <u>multiple</u> or <u>sequential</u> sampling, the decision to accept or reject may be deferred until more than one sample has been analyzed. We shall examine only <u>double sampling</u>, i.e., sampling plans in which no more than two samples are analyzed before a decision is made. The principles used may be applied to higher order sequential sampling.

Generally speaking, a double sampling plan will involve the inspection of fewer items (thereby reducing inspection costs) than a single sampling plan which provides the same protection against type 1 and 2 errors. Furthermore this type of sampling reduces some of the arbitrariness involved in determining significance levels.

The general procedure is as follows. A single sample is taken. If the results of this sample are "extremely consistent" with the hypothesis, the entire lot is accepted. If the results are "extremely inconsistent" the entire lot is rejected. If the results are neither "extremely consistent or inconsistent", i.e., if they are somewhere "in-between", a second sample is taken. The decision to accept or reject will now be based on the nature of the combined samples, i.e., we base our decision upon an examination of the probabilities of obtaining two samples of the kind actually obtained.

The following examples will clarify these terms and the general procedure.

7.81   <u>Manufacturing Example</u>.   The manufacturer who purchases electronic tubes decides to base his decision to accept or reject a shipment on a double sampling plan. He wants to protect himself against lots which are more than five percent defective and, accordingly, poses the hypothesis that the sample obtained comes from a lot which is not more than five percent defective. On the assumption that his hypothesis is true, he outlines the following conditions:

1. If the results of the first sample would be expected to occur only .1 percent (or less) of the time, he will call them "sufficiently inconsistent" and reject the lot. That is, he will accept

a .001 probability of committing a type 1 error on the first sample.

2. If the results of the first sample would be expected to occur more than fifteen percent of the time, they will be considered "sufficiently consistent" and he will accept the lot.

3. If the results would be expected to occur fifteen percent or less of the time, but more than .1 percent of the time, he will take a second sample.

4. If the combined results of the two samples are such that they would occur only one percent (or less) of the time, the hypothesis will be rejected, otherwise it will be accepted. Thus, he will accept a .01 probability of committing a type 1 error on the combined samples.

5. If a decision to accept is made, based on either the results of the first sample alone or the combined samples, the probability of a type 2 error is to be less than or equal to .15 when $\underline{d} \geq .35$.

The problem is to design a sampling plan which will accomplish all these things with the smallest possible sample sizes. For a particular double sampling plan, let:

$\underline{a}_1$ denote the probability that the hypothesis (that $\underline{d} \leq .05$) will be rejected, on the basis of the first sample, when it is actually true;

$\underline{a}_2$ denote the probability that the hypothesis (that $\underline{d} \leq .05$) will be rejected, on the basis of the combined samples, when it is actually true;

$\underline{c}_1$ denote the maximum number of defective items which can be observed, in either the first sample or the combined samples, without causing the rejection of the hypothesis;

$\underline{c}_2$ denote the maximum number of defective items that can be observed in the first sample and still cause the hypothesis to be accepted;

$\underline{e}$ denote the probability of $\underline{c}_2$ or more defectives in the first sample (when $\underline{d} \leq .05$);

$\underline{n}_1$ denote the size of the first sample;

$\underline{n}_2$ denote the size of the second sample;

$\underline{B}_1$ denote the probability that the hypothesis will be accepted, on the basis of the first sample, when $\underline{d}$ is actually $\geq .35$;

$\underline{B}_2$ denote the probability that the hypothesis will be accepted, on the basis of the combined samples, when $\underline{d}$ is actually $\geq .35$.

We must choose n_1, n_2, c_1, and c_2 so that a_1 $\leq .001$, $e > .15$, $a_2 \leq .01$, $B_1 \leq .15$, and $B_2 \leq .15$. The general procedure for solving this problem is as follows:

1. Arbitrarily choose n_1 and determine c_1 and c_2.
2. Determine B_1 for this plan.
3. Repeat the first two steps until a sample size, designated by n_1', is obtained such that the a_1, e, and B_1 conditions are satisfied for n_1, and B_1 not satisfied for $n_1'-1$; i.e., n_1' is the smallest sample size which simultaneously satisfies a_1, e, and B_1.
4. Determine the smallest sample size such that a_2 and B_2 are satisfied for the previously determined c_1. Call this sample size n_3. Then $n_2 = n_3 - n_1$.

We shall now follow this procedure and complete the present example.

We arbitrarily pick a sample size of 6 and set out to determine c_1. If we set $c_1 = 2$, we find (from Eq. 5.6) that $a_1 = .0022$ is the probability of rejecting the hypothesis (the probability of obtaining 3 or more defectives) when $d = .05$. Since $a_1 = .0022 > .001$, 2 is not an acceptable value for c_1. Next, we set $c_1 = 3$ and find that $a_1 = .0001$ is the probability of rejecting the hypothesis (i.e., of obtaining 4 or more defectives) when $d = .05$. Since now $a_1 = .0001 < .001$, 3 is an acceptable value for c_1. Thus, $c_1 = 3$ is the maximum number of defectives that can be observed in a sample of $n = 6$ tubes without causing the hypothesis to be rejected.

Next, we determine c_2. If we set $c_2 = 2$, we find that the probability of 2 or more defectives occurring (if $d = .05$) is $e = .0328$. Since $e = .0328 \leq .15$, we would not accept (or reject) the hypothesis, and hence 2 is not an acceptable value for c_2. However, if we set $c_2 = 1$, we find that the probability of 1 or more defectives occurring (if $d = .05$) is $e = .2649 > .15$. Hence, $c_2 = 1$ is an acceptable value for c_2; i.e., $c_2 = 1$ is the maximum number of defectives that can be observed in a sample of $n = 6$ tubes and still have the hypothesis accepted.

Now we must determine whether the condition for the type 2 error is satisfied for this plan ($n = 6$, $c_2 = 1$). We find that $B_1 = .3191$ is the probability of a type 2 error (the probability of obtaining either 0 or 1 defective items) when $d = .35$. Since $B_1 = .3191 \geq .15$, the present sample size is too small, and the same procedure must be repeated for a larger sample.

A sample size of 8 results in $c_1 = 3$, $c_2 = 1$, but $B_1 = .1691 > .15$, indicating that a still larger sample is required. Finally, a sample size of 9 results in $c_1 = 3$, $c_2 = 1$, and $B_1 = .1211$. n_1 thus equals 9.

Finally, a sample size of 9 results in $c_1 = 3$, $c_2 = 1$, and $B_1 = .1211$. n_1 thus equals 9.

Next, we must determine the smallest n_2 which will satisfy the a_2 and B_2 conditions. Again we employ a trial and error procedure. If the combined sample size (n_3) were arbitrarily set equal to 15, with $c_1 = 3$, a_2 would equal $.0055 < .01$, thereby satisfying the a_2 condition. But $B_2 = .1727 > .15$, which does not satisfy the condition for type 2 errors on the combined sample. However, if the combined sample size were set equal to 16, the reader can verify that, for $c_1 = 3$, we have $a_2 = .0070 < .01$ and $B_2 = .1339 < .15$. Since $n_3 = 16$ and $n_1 = 9$, then $n_2 = 7$.

The required sampling plan is thus one where $n_1 = 9$, $n_2 = 7$, $c_1 = 3$, and $c_2 = 1$.

7.82 OC Curves for Double Sampling Plans.

For the sampling plan just determined, what is the probability of accepting the hypothesis if $d = .1$? A decision to accept the hypothesis can be made either after the first sample is taken or after the second sample is taken. The decision will be made on the basis of the first sample if either 0 or 1 defective items are obtained in the first sample. The decision will be made on the basis of the second sample if either: 1) 2 defective items are obtained in the first sample and 0 or 1 in the second sample, or 2) 3 defective items are selected in the first sample and 0 in the second. These events, together with their probabilities, are summarized in Table 7.6. $P_1(0)$ designates the probability of obtaining 0 defectives in the first sample, $P_2(2)$ the probability of 2 in the second sample, etc. The probabilities of the first two events are determined by applying Eq. 5.6 and those of the last three by applying Eqs. 5.5 and 5.6. Adding these probabilities Eq. 5.4, we determine that the probability of accepting the hypothesis that $d \leq .05$ (when d actually is .1), on the basis of the sampling plan of the preceding section, is .9427.

In a similar fashion, the probabilities of accepting the hypothesis for other d-values with this same sampling plan can be determined. Thus, an operating characteristic curve can be derived for this, and other, double (or higher order) sampling plans, just as in the case of single sampling plans.

TABLE 7.6

PROBABILITY OF ACCEPTING HYPOTHESIS THAT $\underline{d} \leq .05$
WHEN $\underline{d}$ = .10, BASED ON DOUBLE SAMPLING PLAN IN
WHICH $\underline{n}_1$ = 9, $\underline{n}_2$ = 7, $\underline{c}_1$ = 3, $\underline{c}_2$ = 1

Event	Probability of Event
0 defectives in first sample	$\underline{P}_1(0) = .3874$
1 defective in first sample	$\underline{P}_1(1) = .3874$
2 defectives in first sample and 0 in second	$\underline{P}_1(2) \cdot \underline{P}_2(0) = (.1722)(.4783) = .0824$
2 defectives in first sample and 1 in second	$\underline{P}_1(2) \cdot \underline{P}_2(1) = (.1722)(.3720) = .0641$
3 defectives in first sample and 0 in second	$\underline{P}_1(3) \cdot \underline{P}_2(0) = (.0447)(.4783) = \underline{.0214}$
	.9427

7.83   **Marketing Example.** A federal agency conducts a national
survey and finds that college students account for two percent
of the national sales of all brands of filter cigarettes. Firm X,
a manufacturer of filter cigarettes, seeks to determine whether
its sales to college students conform to the national average.
It formulates the hypothesis that $\underline{d}$, the percentage of its sales
accounted for by college students, is no more than two percent.
To test this hypothesis, Firm X decides to adopt a double sampling plan, as follows:

1. If the result of (i.e., the number of college students in) the
first sample of customers would be expected to occur 1 per
cent (or less) of the time if the hypothesis were in fact true, the
hypothesis will be rejected.

2. If the results of the first sample would be expected to
occur more than 25 percent of the time, the hypothesis will be
accepted.

3. If the results would be expected to occur more than 1
percent of the time but 25 percent or less of the time, a second
sample will be taken.

4. If the combined results of the two samples would be expected to occur 2 percent (or less) of the time, the hypothesis will be rejected, otherwise accepted.

5. If a decision to accept is made after the first sample is taken, the probability of a type 2 error is to be less than or equal to .10 when $d \geq .20$; if the decision to accept is made after the second sample has been taken, the probability of a type 2 error is to be less than or equal to .21 when $d \geq .20$.

What sampling plan will satisfy all of these conditions with the smallest possible sample sizes? We must determine n_1, n_2, c_1, and c_2 so that $a_1 \leq .01$, $e > .25$, $a_2 \leq .02$, $B_1 \leq .10$ when $d \geq .20$, and $B_2 \leq .21$ when $d \geq .20$.

Applying the procedure used in the preceding example, the student can find that the desired sampling plan is $n_1 = 11$, $n_2 = 9$, $c_1 = 2$, and $c_2 = 0$. Under this plan, the probability of making a type 1 error because of a decision based only on the first sample is .0012; the probability based on both samples is .0071. The probability of a type 2 error based on a decision involving only the first sample is .0859, while that based on a decision involving both samples is .2061.

7.84   Exercises

1. For the sampling plan derived in Section 7.81, what is the probability of accepting the hypothesis when $d = .01$? $d = .50$?

2. In Section 7.81, assume that $a_1 \leq .01$, $e > .20$, $a_2 \leq .05$, and $B_1 \leq .10$ and $B_2 \leq .15$ when $d \geq .3$. Design a double sampling plan which minimizes the number of items inspected. Assume the hypothesis being tested is that $d \leq .20$.

3. In Section 7.83, show that the plan $n_1 = 10$, $n_2 = 9$, $c_1 = 2$, $c_2 = 0$ does not satisfy the specified contitions.

4. In Section 7.83, show that the plan $n_1 = 11$, $n_2 = 8$, $c_1 = 2$, and $c_2 = 0$ does not satisfy the specified conditions.

5. In the sampling plan developed in Section 7.83, what is the probability of a type 1 error if $d = .02$? $d = .06$? $d = .01$?

6. In the sampling plan developed in Section 7.83, what is the probability of a type 2 error if $d = .06$? $d = .01$? $d = .10$?

7.9   ACCEPTANCE/RECTIFICATION AND AOQL

As a final application from the field of acceptance sampling, we shall examine an acceptance sampling scheme typically referred to as an acceptance/rectification plan. Under this type scheme, if the given sampling plan (derived according to the method described in the preceding sections) leads to a rejection of the hypothesis, the shipment or lot is not returned. Instead, the shipment is 100 percent inspected and defective items are replaced by good items, so that the number of items originally in the lot is maintained. This lot is then employed in the manufacturing process.

Assume that the only possible factor contributing to a defective final product is the item taken from the purchased lot. Then final products manufactured from items contained in rejected, and therefore 100 percent screened, lots will be 0 percent defective. Final products manufactured from items contained in initially accepted lots will have a proportion defective equivalent to the proportion defective in the submitted lots. For any sampling plan, the maximum possible proportion defective in the outgoing product on the average in the long run (on the average for many submitted lots) can be computed. This maximum possible proportion defective is called the average outgoing quality limit (AOQL). The following example will show how to compute the AOQL.

In a single sampling plan, $c = 1$ and $n = 20$. Table 7.7 shows the probabilities of accepting, under this sampling plan, lots having various proportions defective. Since, as throughout this chapter, it is assumed that the sample size is very small relative to the lot size, these probabilities have been determined by applying Eq. (5.6). The third column of Table 7.7 shows the average proportion defective in the outgoing product. The method by which this column is derived can be explained by examining the derivation of the first figure, .0368.

If many (say z, where z is a large number) equal-sized lots, each with $d = .05$, were submitted over a period of time, 73.58 percent of them (i.e., $.7358z$) would be accepted without the benefit of any screening. Final products produced from these $.7358z$ lots would therefore be 5 percent defective. However, in the long run $1 - .7358z = 26.42$ percent of all submitted lots $(.2642z)$ would be initially rejected, screened, and then entered into the manufacturing process. Final products produced from these $.2642z$ lots would therefore be 0 percent defective. Thus, in the long run, the average proportion defective of final products would be $[(.05)(.7358\underline{z}) + (.00)(.2642\underline{z})]/\underline{z} = .0368$. The other figures in the third column of Table 7.7 are determined similarly.

TABLE 7.7

DETERMINATION OF AVERAGE OUTGOING QUALITY LIMIT FOR SINGLE SAMPLING PLAN IN WHICH $\underline{c} = 1$ AND $\underline{n} = 20$

Proportion Defective in Submitted Lots	Probability of Accepting Lot	Average Proportion Defective in the Outgoing Product
.05	.7358	.0368
.10	.3917	.0392
.15	.1756	.0263
.20	.0692	.0138
.25	.0243	.0061
.30	.0076	.0023
.35	.0021	.0008
.40	.0005	.0002
.45	.0001	.0000
.50	.0000	.0000

Examining this column, we see that the maximum average proportion defective is approximately .0392. The AOQL will be realized, for this sampling plan, for submitted lots in which $.05 < \underline{d} < .15$.

7.91   Exercises

1. Given the single sampling plan $\underline{n} = 10$ and $\underline{c} = 0$, determine the AOQL for an acceptance/rectification scheme.

2. Given the single sampling plan $\underline{n} = 6$ and $\underline{c} = 1$, determine the AOQL.

SELECTED BIBLIOGRAPHY

Bowman, Edward H. and Fetter, Robert B., Analysis for Production Management. Homewood, Ill.: Richard D. Irwin, Inc., rev. ed., 1967.

Buffa, Elwood S., Models for Production and Operations Management. New York: John Wiley and Sons, Inc., 1963.

Duncan, Acheson J., Quality Control and Industrial Statistics. Homewood, Ill.: Richard D. Irwin, Inc., 3rd ed., 1965.

Goldberg, Samuel, Probability. Englewood Cliffs, N.J.: Prentice-Hall, Inc., 1960.

Huntsberger, David V., Elements of Statistical Inference. Boston: Allyn and Bacon, Inc., 1961.

Kattsoff, Louis O., and Simone, Albert J., Finite Mathematics, with Applications in the Social and Management Sciences, Ch. 4, New York: McGraw-Hill Book Co., Inc., 1965.

McMillan, Claude and Gonzalez, Richard F., Systems Analysis, A Computer Approach to Decision Models. Homewood, Ill.: Richard D. Irwin, Inc., 1965.

Prabhu, N.U., Queues and Inventories. New York: John Wiley and Sons, Inc., 1965.

Schlaifer, Robert, Probability and Statistics for Business Decisions, New York: Mc Graw-Hill Book Co., Inc., 1959.

Wessel, Robert H., Willett, Edward R., and Simone, Albert J., Statistics as Applied to Economics and Business. New York: Holt, Rinehart and Winston, Inc., rev. ed., 1965.

INDEX

161

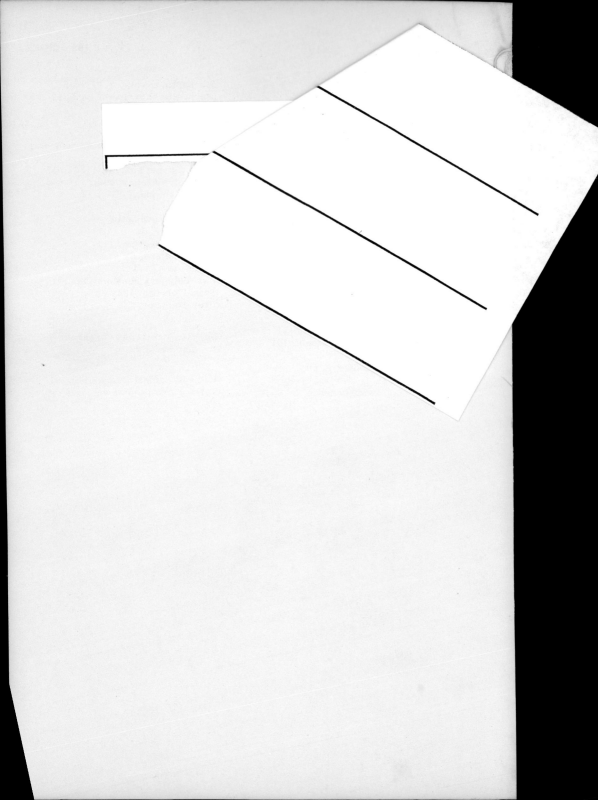